YOUR FEET ARE KILLING ME!

Also by John D. Vose:

THE LADY OF CONNEMARA

YOUR FEET ARE
KILLING ME!

John D. Vose

UNITED WRITERS
CORNWALL

Published by
UNITED WRITERS PUBLICATIONS
Trevail Mill - Zennor - St. Ives
Cornwall

ISBN 901976 46 6

Printed in Great Britain by
United Writers Publications
Cornwall

I dedicate this book to all
Chiropody Students

Chapter One

The city of Barnfield embraced me like a giant stone octopus. Taxis, buses, lorries and cars sped through the tentacle-like streets, the whole mass heaving and fermenting in the teatime rush hour.

I was waiting for a 6A bus to take me to Gadsbury, a district of Barnfield in which I was a complete stranger.

"The 6A," a former student at the foot hospital had told me, "goes right past the gates."

And that's exactly what it did for me - went right past. But that was something I only found out when I, the last perplexed passenger, reached the terminus.

I listened attentively as each stop was most faithfully called out by a conscientious conductor. "Miller's Garage" - "Eye Hospital" - "Ice Rink" - "Dog and Duck" - "Corn Exchange" - "Four Lane Ends" - "Picture House".

We were arriving at the terminus when the conductor looked at me like the Ancient Mariner.

"Blimey! I forgot yer. But I did call."

"I didn't hear you mention the chiropody hospital."

"But I did. Didn't you hear me yell, 'Corn Exchange'? That's it. Get it?"

I got the joke - such as it was - but not the stop. And the only way to reach it was to walk, carrying a heavy case, most of the way up a one-in-seven hill.

"Goin' to 'ave yer feet done, are yer?" he said. "Believe me, yer'll need it by the time yer. . ."

"I'm not going there for treatment," I told him. "I'm going to train as a chiropodist."

"Oh, one of them!" It was obvious that he thought I was seeking to enter the very lowest possible occupation.

The driver, who had joined us by this time, shared his view. "Millions of miles of feet!" he said. "What a prospect!"

"Still," said the conductor, "Foot specialists come in useful at times. I know that."

"Don't we all?" responded the driver.

7

As I trudged up that seemingly endless hill, I began to feel that I should need treatment when I reached the hospital. But when I finally reached its broad stone portals, my immediate need was a meal and lashings of tea. Neither was readily available. I was gazing up at a peculiar object mounted on a plaque. It was anything but a foot, as one might have expected. And when I left the hospital I was still ignorant of what it was.

I was accosted by a man in brown overalls. "Where you stayin', son? "

"Mrs Crabshaw's, 6, St. Nicholas Road. "

He took my case, eyeing me with a pity he might have reserved for a man entering the condemned cell. "I hope you've got a strong stomach, " he said.

"You know it, then? "

"I'm the hospital caretaker. " He began to move away from the main building. "It's closed now, so I'll take you round to Mrs Crabshaw's. "

"Is her food uneatable? " I asked apprehensively.

"Not uneatable. Just indigestible. " Noticing my crestfallen manner, he added, "You'll survive. They all do. Mrs Crabshaw's not lost a student yet. "

Noticing I was gazing enquiringly at the plaque over the main door, he said, "Can't you read French, either? "

"It's Latin, " I informed him.

"Well, it's ruddy Dutch to me. They reckon it means, 'Be sure when your patient goes, he always leaves with all his toes'. "

As he ushered me across the grounds to a side lawn, the caretaker informed me that Mrs Crabshaw's was a large Victorian residence. Containing sixteen bedrooms, it dated back to the days when Gadsbury had been a paradise for cotton kings, shipping owners and engineering magnates.

"Had a marvellous time, they had, " he said. "Life for them was all wine and skittles and women. 'Specially women. There were great goings-on, I can tell you. Talk about orgies. . . "

"I wasn't, " I interrupted.

"But I am. And they were worth talking about. My old man was the gateman on the entrance. Private park in those days. Could have written a book could my old man. "

He had no need to tell me we had arrived at Mrs Crabshaw's. The building thrust upwards, as firmly planted as the pyramids, five frowning storeys with proudly aggressive bay windows on the ground floor.

"Mrs Crabshaw's residence for Chiropodial Gentlemen, "

8

the caretaker announced. "At least, that's how she describes it to the vicar."

"She's religious, is she?"

"She's good with the words."

"But not with the works, it seems?"

"You'll find out." He handed me my case. "Good luck!" His tone suggested the Dantean warning, 'Abandon hope all ye who enter here'.

Mrs Crabshaw was by no means what the caretaker had led me to expect. She was stout and bosomy and generously chinned and had smooth skin and a wealth of lacquered hair dotted with myriad sparkling flecks of silver.

"Ah, the last of the few!" she greeted me. "You are. . .?"

"Vose, "I volunteered.

"Yes, yes, of course. Mr Vose. Welcome, welcome, welcome! How nice to have yet another boy!" She held my hand in both hers. "A good boy, too, I'm sure. One who appreciates hospitality and concern and good food. Rather thin, aren't we. Building up is what you need."

"Right now, I would appreciate almost any sort of meal."

She might have said - 'That is the sort you will get!' - Instead, she said, "Your room is number 10, on the third floor."

I hauled my heavy case up the rickety flights of stairs and found I shared the room with two other students who were sorting out their stuff before tea.

The bedroom was rather like a public hall, large and sparsely furnished, with nine-foot high walls colour-washed because, Mrs Crabshaw claimed, they were too high to paper. In winter it was like an igloo, the institutional lino numbing bare feet, no matter how warm the weather. The three ancient beds had iron frames decorated with a quartet of brass balls, one at each corner, with one notable exception. That bed had only three brass balls and, naturally, it was referred to as the pawn bed. I was informed by the caretaker at a later date that the house had at one time been the residence of Miss Pankhurst the suffragette.

Alick was a Black, about thirty years of age, whose real name was Santiago Galikeer. Powerfully built with a proud bearing. When he shook my hand his powerful grip had me trembling right down to my foundations.

"Me glad to meet you," he said.

My eyes watering, I summoned sufficient insincerity to say that I was glad to meet him, and made a mental note never

9

to place my hand in his ever again.

Seamus Toomey, of County Cork, also shook hands. He was pleasant and good-looking and I took to him at once.

"Sure he doesn't know his own strength, " he said, indicating Alick. "His father didn't either. "

"His father? " I echoed, puzzled.

"Sure. His father. He is some sort of king in one of the more remote wastelands of Africa. Had fifty-two wives and the bloody fool slept with his dad. " A pillow hit him full in the face.

I whistled. "My God! One for every week of the year. Was that the idea? "

"More or less. He fathered a hundred and ten children. "

"All by himself? "

"I told you - he didn't know his own strength. " He nodded towards Alick, who was grinning broadly, evidently proud of his father's prowess. "He's a prince. "

"And he intends to become a chiropodist! " I exclaimed.

"For the sake of his tribe, " said Seamus. "That's it, isn't it, Alick? "

"Man, that is it. My people wear shoes. Never wore shoes before. Never wore anything before. My people like shoes, but not their feet. "

"I see what you mean, " I said. "They're developing the usual foot troubles? "

"Yes. They would rather wear shoes round their necks. But that not civilised. My father say they must be worn on feet. "

It turned out that there were ten chiropody students domiciled at No. 6, St. Nicholas Road. Four were second-year students, the rest of us were raw rookies. The dominant personality in the digs was undoubtedly Clive, who was a few years older than the rest of us. He became known to the first-year students as The Oracle. He knew all about everybody, including the staff at the hospital, the staff at No. 6, all the students and, not least, Mrs Crabshaw. He always wore a spotted bow tie and spoke with an accent that he had obviously most carefully cultivated. We reckoned he'd be able to charge at least forty per cent extra with such an impressive accent.

The evening meal was a sample of things to come. Clive sat at the head of the table, his own blue napkin protecting his shirt and trousers and held in place by a silver pin in the shape of a foot.

"Shall we have the usual tanner on who spots it first, gentlemen? " Clive asked. "For the benefit of newcomers I must explain that we call it find the egg or sausage, whatever happens to be hiding coyly beneath the potatoes. Believe it not but Charles over there actually found a pork chop. But that was a freak."

At that moment a young woman of plain features, but blessed with an arresting figure, arrived carrying a heavily laden tray. She was wearing a low-cut dress that showed a generous depth of cleavage. The students watched her every movement while striving to give the impression that their attention was elsewhere.

Only when Ada had left did we turn our attention to what she had left us with. Ostensibly, our plates were ladened with potato.

"Don't be dismayed," Clive said. "Somewhere, nestling beneath the solanum tuberosum, is either a sausage or an egg or, though most improbably, a piece of meat an inch square."

"Man," said Alick, "does we have to dig for it?"

"Man," said Clive, "You does! No spears allowed, your Highness, only knives and forks. But we are all risking a tanner on being the first to uncover the mystery. The winner takes all. And you win, not by cheating, but by eating. Everybody ready. . .? Go!"

Potatoes proved to be more than the staple diet at No.6. They made up some ninety per cent of the whole annual menu.

"I'm wondering," said Seamus, "if Mrs C. imagines potatoes are an aphrodisiac."

"Just a stringently economical diet," said Clive without pausing in his eating. "You are beginning a long period of trial by monotony."

It was, in fact, potatoes, potatoes all the way and, apart from left-overs fried for breakfast, they were always served mashed, or 'creamed', as Mrs C. would say. The one redeeming feature was anticipating what lay under the mash.

As far as lodgers went, it was strictly a male establishment. But the staff consisted of 'Our Ada' and a couple of females who came in daily to do housework, but judging by our diet it was mainly to peel potatoes. I soon found out why the unmade road was deeply rutted outside our digs, for every day, without fail, the local greengrocer would make a delivery of potatoes.

Clive informed us that 'Our Ada' was partial to good-looking young men. Whether he included me in his generalisation I didn't know. Although she was plain, her smile did something for her, and she smiled seraphically when a student 'accidentally' stumbled against her or saved her from falling

11

by placing his arms about her. Many learned more about the female anatomy in those brief encounters than they learned about the human foot during three years of study.

On the first day of our course we paraded before the Principal and the lecturers of the School of Chiropody. Although I had looked up the meaning of the word chiropody in the dictionary and read that it involved the treatment of corns, bunions, etcetera, I really had no idea what I had let myself in for. The truth was that, being unable to find my way into any other calling or profession, I had plunged into chiropody as an act of desperation. Some men take to drink, others to the mountains and wild remote regions of the globe, when they feel they are failures. I took to feet.

Miss Hotchkiss, the Principal, had the task of introducing us to the mysteries of the profession. Tall and thin, and in her early forties, she was never at ease in the presence of the male, and so she stuttered and fluttered, making lavish use of her hands to add emphasis to her words. She was also marred by being an arrant snob. She knew only the best people, read only the best books, listened only to the best music and, of course, was in the best profession. She made that abundantly clear from the outset.

"Sher-opody," she said, "is a noble calling." She spoke in a rather high-pitched, pseudo-St. Albans accent. "F-f-feet are f-foundations. The whole human f-f-family stands or falls by its f-f-feet." She was gesturing towards her toes as she spoke. "There are those in-in-insensitive persons who remark scornfully that you cannot g-g-get lower than feet. Thereby they display their abysmal ignorance." She flung out a hand in a dismissive gesture. "And we f-f-flatly refute their c-claim. W-w-we stand up, not afraid to b-b-be c-c-counted. We are on our t-t-toes."

"On other people's toes, surely," a voice said.

But Miss Hotchkiss was now in her stride, voicing an oft delivered and much rehearsed panegyric. "Without our splendid c-c-calling," she said, "men could not climb Everest, r-r-run a mile in less than f-f-four minutes, journey into space or even take a short w-w-walk. It is w-w-we who keep the human r-r-race mobile. It is we who ensure that people c-c-can move c-c-comfortably from one place to another. W-w-we are the p-p-pain removers. W-w-we give ease and f-f-freedom. Was it not Sh-Sh-Shakespeare who said, 'Her foot speaks'? And was it not T-T-Tennyson who said, 'And feet like sunny gems on an English green'?"

"I thought it was D.H. Lawrence who said that?" the same

12

voice said.

But Miss Hotchkiss, who seemed not to have heard the voice, and who had certainly no knowledge of the words and works of Lawrence, went blithely on.

"You m-m-may spend much of your l-l-life kneeling at the f-f-feet of people. But r-r-remember that you st-st-stoop to conquer. The sher-opodist holds his head high. He is an honoured member of society. Indeed, he c-c-can make the large c-c-claim that he k-k-keeps the nation on its feet. How proud we all are that we - yes, we - have been chosen to serve in this regal profession!"

Having given the impression that we were treading in the steps of kings and princes, she yielded place to Mr Stubbins, the Senior Lecturer in Chiropody. He proved to be a very different sort of person. He was a small, tubby man, with a rubicund and very round face. His bald head had a thick halo of snow-white hair, his eyes twinkled and his mouth curved upwards, ready on the slightest provocation to break into laughter. He was, in fact, known with some affection as 'Pickwick' Stubbins.

"Gentlemen," he began in a brisk and buoyant manner, 'the overall title of my series of lectures is 'Chiropody - My Foot! And I would point out at the outset that the examination and treatment are limited to the foot. Anything above that is no concern of yours. Being in your first or second youth, you may well imagine that there are more interesting regions of the anatomy at higher levels. Gentlemen, I do not quarrel with that. However, feet also, I assure you, can be beautiful, though you are more likely to see feet of the opposite type, so concentrate your attention to these appendages, gentlemen - it is possible to be turned on, I believe that is the popular phrase, by a handsome pair of feet. We must get our kicks somehow! There are cases on record of chiropodists - male chiropodists as distinct from the female variety - who have misled patients - female patients usually under thirty years of age and with exemplary legs - into believing that, in order to make a correct analysis of what was to be done for a corn on the end of a big toe, it was necessary for him to palpate the patient's knees and thighs."

There was an outbreak of laughter.

"This," Mr Stubbins smiled, "is putting pleasure higher than business, a course not to be commended. The conscientious chiropodist - and you will notice, gentlemen, that I pronounce the word as 'kiropody' and not as 'sheropody' - confines himself to the feet and the feet only. I do not need to remind you that this is an age of specialisation. At the beginning of this century, the body, for medical and surgical purposes, was divided into seven parcels. Now the number is over fifty, and you may well live to see the day when there is a chiropodist for the right foot and a chiropodist for the left foot. In other words, feet are most complex and intricate appendages, calling for immense study. "

A sigh rose from the audience.

"Exactly, " said Stubbins. "A daunting prospect. But also a most fascinating one. Also entertaining. Have fun with feet. That may seem to you rather whimsical, but we would have much less fun without them. Now, kindly take a look at this. "

He touched a switch and a large sheet unfolded itself to cover the blackboard. The foot, much enlarged, with every bone and ligament exposed, appeared to me as the most involved piece of mechanism I had ever seen. It made the interior of a computer appear comically simple in comparison. My heart sank at the sight. Suddenly the magnitude of what I had let myself in for engulfed me. I experienced a panic which sent alternating hot flushes and cold shivers down my neck to my toes. Did I really want to be a chiropodist? What lunacy had possessed me to embark on such a course? Suddenly a lifetime on social security seemed as attractive as eternity in a Mohammedan paradise, complete with roses and houris.

"I notice some of you have blenched, " Stubbins was saying. "It seems that I have put my foot right in it. " He chuckled at his little joke, but no first-year student so much as smiled. His persistent punning was to become quite tiresome after a while. " But let us remember, gentlemen, that, like every other science, chiropody was once the province of amateurs. It was indeed a side-line of farriers and barbers. " He chuckled. "Barbers! Head and feet. That's what I call going to two extremes at once. But our attention must remain riveted on the foot. We must remember that feet can cause the most exquisite pain, can lead to fatigue and even to despair. In former days, men seeking sainthood often placed dried peas in their shoes, believing that suffering promoted saintliness. That gives us some measure as to how tormentingly painful the feet can be. For this reason, gentlemen, we must treat feet with the respect - I might even say the reverence - they deserve. "

When we were back at No. 6 after that first lecture, Seamus said, "I'm telling you I feel as if I was in that fatal charge of the Light Brigade. Heading straight for destruction. "

"We're members of the First Foot, " I told him. "We go

14

to our doom without equestrian benefit and fortified with nothing more than a diet of mashed potatoes. "

Mr Stubbins, who revelled in his profession, waxed almost lyrical in his lectures. And when dealing with the common corn he excelled himself.

"Corn, " he began, "has a number of connotations. It is grown grain, which, as I am sure you are aware, includes oats. " He paused for the laughter to subside. "Another kind of corn, " he resumed, "may refer to some of my jokes. But we are concerned only with the corn that burgeons and blooms on feet, although it can blossom on the hands and on the elbows. It is prosaically described as a small, hard growth resulting from an increase of thickness of cuticle, caused by pressure or friction. A more technical definition is a circumscribed tycosis of the stratum corneum of the epidermis. But no patient will want to know that. Nor will it help him or her to know that the corn, in certain of its aspects, is a great friend. Tribesmen in Ethiopia, for instance, who have no footwear, are provided by a bountiful nature with a thickening of the skin on the soles and heels of their feet which give them greater protection than the stoutest leather. But your client is not likely to live in Ethiopia, although I'm told Mr Galikeer is returning to his native land when qualified. He is more likely to live in Wandsworth or Wigan or, God help him, in Workington or Wombell. And he will almost certainly regard his corn as an enemy that must be rooted out. " He paused and smiling ineffably added, "To quote Shakespeare, 'And there's the rub'. "

Constant note-taking became the order of the day at the lectures as Stubbins rattled away, waxing eloquent upon his beloved subject - feet. We soon found that they were most complex, no longer were they plates of meat, they were, to give the Latin name, Podi.

To him the common or garden corn was like the malignant tumour is to the brain surgeon. It took on grandiose and terrifying proportions. It seemed beyond me to even fathom the deep mysteries with which he surrounded the corn.

"No matter what skill chiropodists may show in dealing with the general afflictions of the foot, or what prowess at operating he may have developed, there can be little doubt that his greatest asset is the ability to painlessly and cleverly enucleate a corn. They do not only occur on feet. They are found on the hands of bricklayers, on the elbows of draughts-men and on one occasion I even removed one from the knee of a nun. "

15

The silence that gripped the lecture hall was doom laden.

Slowly and with great emphasis, Stubbins said, "Corn in the field has roots, but the corn on the foot has no roots. I repeat, gentlemen, it has no roots at all."

A prophecy that the world would spin off its axis in about five minutes could not have created a greater sensation. This was iconoclasm. It was sacrilege. Blasphemy.

I found myself recalling my father's corn - a constant and most unwelcome companion throughout his adult life. A variety of surgeons and chiropodists, not to mention a quack who was said to cure everything, including mental instability, mating failures on the part of a husband or wife and any growth on man or beast or even mothers-in-law, had told my father the same thing. All they had to do was remove the root and the corn would trouble him no more. Again and again, all had assured him, after exercising their skills on the excrescence that they had, indeed, eradicated the root.

And all, alas, had been wrong. Within days of the corn being excised, it began to appear again. Steadily it grew, becoming with enlargement ever more painful. Father would limp, he would grumble, he would wince. He caused near chaos in shoe-shops in his search for the right type of shoe he could wear to accommodate his corn. His proper size was nine, but he needed an eleven to avoid pressure on the sensitive hump of tissue. But size eleven were so loose on his feet they were like flippers. In an effort to meet his need, the shop assistants would have the floor choked with boxes, as Father tried on pair after pair. Despairing managers would find themselves climbing to bring down the bottom box on the top shelf, all to no purpose.

"I know!" Father cried out on one memorable occasion, when he had exhausted the whole male stock of shoes in Freeman, Hardy and Willis, and brought the staff to the verge of mutiny.

"Yes?" said a perspiring manager. "What do you know, sir?"

"I need size nine for my left foot, which is the right size, and size eleven for my right foot. That is the wrong size, but it will provide for my corn, allowing me to walk comfortably."

"A most excellent idea, sir," said the manager.

"So," said my father, pointing to a number nine, "I'll have that shoe," then, pointing to a number eleven, "and I'll have that shoe."

"You will have to buy both pairs, sir."

"Both!" Father had gone red about the neck and white

about the gills. "But I only want a nine for my left and an eleven for. . ."

"I know very well what you want, sir." There was a distinctly double meaning to the manager's words. "I also know what you need. But we sell shoes in pairs, except in very special cases. And yours, if I may say so, is not a special case."

"You dare to say that to me!" Father was showing signs of squaring up to the manager. And as Father had gained several awards in judo and karate, and the manager was a mere five foot five inches, there was a real danger that this branch of Freeman, Hardy and Willis would soon be appointing a new man to take charge. "Let me tell you," Father was saying, almost choking on his wrath, "that my case is the most special you've ever had."

As a growing group of unserved customers were looking on with a degree of interest usually reserved for a royal wedding or a public execution, the situation called for quick thinking and instant action. Neither emerged. Instead, my father, his face a fierce mask of determination and within inches of the manager's, who was blinking, gasping and perspiring, demanded, "You sell shoes, don't you?"

"Of course." The little man, though terrified, was by no means petrified. Beneath his film of sweat he wore the expression of one who was not to be intimidated. "But I must remind you that we sell them in pairs."

"And," my father said between clenched teeth, "that is exactly what I want. Two makes a pair. And that size nine and that size eleven together make a pair. That is what I want, and as sure as shoe-shop managers are as expendable as used washing-up water, that is what I mean to have." And to give emphasis to his words his hands came up in the most menacing of all karate positions.

That manager was already as good as dead.

That is, he would have been had it not happened that the little man, realising his danger, took a step back, intending to retreat. Fortunately for him, he stepped on one of the numerous shoes littering the floor, losing his balance. To save himself, he took a very quick and very firm step forward.

The howl of anguish that leapt from my father's lips made it known over a wide area just what had happened. The manager had stamped on Father's corn. Water starting from his eyes, colour fleeing from his face, he was striving to balance on his left foot while seeking in vain to nurse his injured right extremity. From his lips issued a spate of words which I, in

17

my youthful innocence, took to be from the Greek he had
learned while fighting in the second world war in the uplands
of Thessalonika. With his right foot in his hands, he epitomised
perfectly the phrase 'hopping mad'.

The manager, however, aware that a large crowd had
gathered both in and outside the shop, and realising many of
the onlookers might well be under the impression that my
father was the victim of a pair of badly-made or ill-fitting
shoes, and that some very bad publicity might be carried far
and wide, decided to act.

"Sir," he said, "you are quite right. Widdop, Windhill
and Walker sell a very inferior type of shoe. We have had
numerous complaints about the quality of their materials and
workmanship. But we are only satisfied when our customers
are satisfied. You shall have the pair you asked for."

Corns, I was to find out, are classified just as boarding
houses and hotels are in Blackpool or Brighton.

(1) Heloma Molle (soft corn) usually found between the
toes which rub together, thus producing the corn which
thrives in warm perspirant conditions.

(2) Heloma Durum (hard corn) is the most common type.

(3) Heloma Vasculare (known in the profession as
bleeders.)

(4) Heloma Neuro-Vasculare (painful bleeders)

These last two bring more oaths to the mouths of chiropodists than any others.

(5) Heloma Milleare. Seed corns which are often multiple
in distribution on the soles of the feet.

During tea one evening in the second week, Mrs Crabshaw
announced that a new lodger was joining us and this would
mean a shuffle round of sleeping quarters. It turned out to be
a student I had only exchanged nods with up to then. Little did
I realise, as he stood there looking like a commercial trav-
eller down on his luck with two bulging, decrepit suitcases
in his hands, that he was destined to play a large part in my
professional future.

His full name was Hezikiah Abel Solomon Hymans. Solly
was a huge, fat Jew boy who had given up the idea of religion
and had decided on chiropody as a profession. He wore a black
skull cap and was addicted to beer which undoubtedly was the
reason he'd found he'd never make a Rabbi. A drunken

18

chiropodist would be bad enough but imagine the bother a drunken Rabbi could cause. Those circumcision knives are mighty sharp. Solly was seventeen stone and my first shock came when Mrs Crabshaw told me that he and I would be sharing the double bed by the window. I was the thinnest of the other students and would just about fit in the space Solly left in the bed. His other features were a spotty face and a pointed beard. I'd only ever read about such people in novels. I'd never imagined they really existed. I found, too, that he was possessed of several irritating habits, one of which was hanging his socks over the head of the bed. More often than not they'd fall on my face during the night. Still, it was good experience for a man who was studying to be a chiropodist.

Chapter Two

So gradually the weeks, then the months, rolled by and as we first-year students slowly came to terms with the course, Stubbins continued to pump his profound knowledge into us so that, if we took notice, we couldn't help but become first-class practitioners. But it was the practical side of chiropody that was the most hair-raising. Before we performed on real flesh and blood patients, we practised on each other. We would take it in turns to become patient and operator. The first time I sat in the high chair, I had ten fits for my feet had been coated with daubs of wax to represent hard skin. Solly sat in the operator's chair, scalpel in trembling hand; trembling not with nerves I hasten to add, but with an overdose of Hignett's best bitter at the 'Bull and Trumpet' where he did all his swotting. When the wax had set, he pushed the scalpel jerkily towards my foot. I shut my eyes in fear, my foot was shaking like a jelly. If we could only have coordinated our jerks all would have been fine, but as it was there could only be one result.

"For goodness sake, Solly, be careful!" I hissed at him.

"Keep your bloody foot still, and I'll try to be," came the sympathetic reply.

For a few seconds all went well. Then I heard, "Blast it, I've cut you!" My foot was stinging like fury.

Fortunately, one of the clinicians came to my aid before he turned my foot into a red mass.

She stopped the bleeding with 'Ferric Perchloride', the 'Chiropodists' Friend', and proceeded to give Solly a lesson in paring wax without turning my foot into a battle field. Qualified though she was, I was still shaking with fear and was jolly glad to get my shoes and socks on again. I don't know if the clinician expected revenge on my part but she separated us for the afternoon session and Solly had to operate on Alick's feet. Now, even to a fully-fledged chiropodist, a black foot is more difficult to operate on than a white one. The corns and callosities are not so clearly defined against a black back-

20

ground, so poor Alick had rather a handicap, and the poor chap got rather badly cut about the feet. One night, before he got into bed, I counted seven strips of plaster on his feet. But he never really complained, and took his lot philosophically though he did once remark in the privacy of our bedroom:

"Ah sure wish to hell you'd go easy on the beer the night before you does mah feet, Solly."

Of course, operating on real, live feet with real, live corns was a tricky business at first, but let me hasten to assure any would-be 'guinea-pigs' that the treatment by students is carried out under strict supervision from the qualified staff.

The case cards fascinated me, especially the strange signs and drawings done by students on the printed feet. Every patient had one which was filed away in a cabinet. They were stamped as follows:

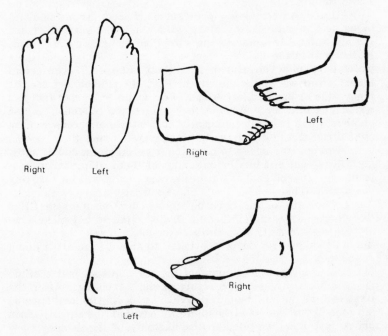

Anatomical disorders and the sites of corns, et cetera, could be drawn on the diagrams.

21

The card was filled up after each treatment so that a continuous record of treatments was kept. Details such as diabetes and other important information are marked on the cards so that a complete picture of the patient's health can be seen at a glance. For instance, rheumatoid arthritis is a particularly painful complaint which affects the smaller bones such as those of the hands and feet. Great tenderness is felt so that the chiropodist is especially gentle when moving the joints. The trained chiropodist is often able to assess the general health of a patient by the condition of the feet. But one particular reference fascinated me. It appeared quite often on the case cards. N.O.B. printed on the top right-hand corner. This intrigued me and I noticed that the patient was usually of the bad-tempered variety - the initials obviously stood for some kind of nervous disorder.

However, I was soon to find out that I was totally wrong when Miss Hotchkiss summoned the students to a sudden meeting in the clinic.

"It s-seems that the profession of Sher-sher-opody is being held to ridicule by some students, " she said, "I refer mainly to the horseplay in the clinic and lecture rooms. Also to the mutilation of case cards. I have here six c-c-cards which have been vandalised. I can think of no other expression. I am afraid we at the Barnfield Foot Hospital do not see the funny side of the idiotic jottings. For instance, some fool has written on this one, 'What a feat to do these f-f-feet', and on another some imbecile of equally low intelligence has written 'The dirtiest f-feet in Barnfield. Only w-washes them once a year whether she needs to or not'. It is most unethical, most unprofessional and totally unworthy of medical practitioners. In future, anyone caught mutilating case cards will be severely dealt with. That is all. "

I was still in the dark but found out from the sage Clive that N.O.B. meant Nasty Old B . . ., there being several alternatives to suit the occasion. Needless to say, the practice did not stop and no doubt continues to this day in all training schools.

The study of the anatomy of the leg and foot is one of the most important aspects of a chiropodist's training. After the first lecture on this subject delivered by a visiting orthopaedic surgeon from the local hospital, I realised with a sudden shock just how complicated the anatomy of the whole body must be, and how difficult it must be for a medical student to become a fully-fledged G.P. and this is only one part of their training. My concern was only with the anatomy of the leg and foot yet, at first, I was convinced it was beyond me. Twenty-six bones in the foot alone, it seemed impossible. Then there are the muscles: Gastrocnemius, Plantaris, Soleus, Peroneus Longus, Flexor Longus, etc. It was bad enough remembering the names, let alone what they did. Anterior Annular Ligament, Tendon Flexor Longus, and Tendon Peroneus Brevis in the foot, and they are only a few - mix these with the bones such as Tibia, Fibula, Cuboid, Femur, Internal Cunieform, Scaphoid, Astragalus, and Oscalsis plus all the nerve endings, Veins, Ligaments, Arteries and Capillaries and you have an anatomical cocktail lethal enough to make the raw first-year student realise just what he's let himself in for. It's brain beating stuff to be banged in by repetitive study. This, to me, was by far the toughest subject of the whole course and made one realise how right Stubbins had been when he told us how vastly more informed we would be than those chiropodists who hadn't taken a formal course - provided we passed, of course.

I began to grow envious of those 'so-called practitioners' as Stubbins referred to them, who had got their diplomas by diverse means. In days long gone labels from Sattersthwaite's red cabbage jars - send twenty-five and you could be a masseur, thirty a dentist and they were just working on a crash course for doctors (fifty labels) when the Medical Council stepped in and had them stopped. They reckoned it was getting as bad as America where a man could buy diplomas at ten dollars apiece and end up having so many brass plates he'd be so busy polishing them that he wouldn't have time to practise.

Stubbins swore to us that such things had happened and he was dead against people who pulled the profession down into the mud.

So it was that the ideals of the purist were planted in my soul, and I got down to the job of learning this complicated and strange structure of the leg and foot. It amuses me to look back now and bring to mind the peculiar and varied ways we had of learning our subject.

Solly, needless to say, took his books to the 'Bull and Trumpet' where he pondered over them, helped by the inspiration of Hignett's bitter. It was amazing how he could sit in a corner of the tap room with the hullabaloo of dominoes and darts all around him, but, like all eccentrics, he did things in his own way.

Alick was a calypso fanatic and would chant out an old song of the deep south in a voice somewhere between Shirley Bassey and Paul Robeson.

"Yar toe bone connects-a-to yar ankle bone . . . yar ankle bone connects-a-to yar heel bone . . . yar heel bone connects-a-to yar leg bone, and so says the word of the Lord."

He'd accompany himself by banging Mrs Crabshaw's tin kettle with one of her potato knives.

The corridor which ran from the main lecture room to the medicament store on the second floor became known as 'grope alley' for, after dark, more anatomy was learned there than in any other place in the hospital, for the real life structures of the female students were far more interesting than the pictures in the text book.

One of the more colourful lodgers at Mrs Crabshaw's 'Residence for Chiropodial Gentlemen' was our Irish friend Seamus Henry Dominic Toomey, to give him his full title. He was well over six feet and broad with it and hailed from County Cork with an accent as thick as draught Guinness. To me, he was the typical Dublin copper. Amiable, huge and splayfooted, not to mention a rugged handsomeness which appealed very strongly to Ada Crabshaw. But Seamus expressed no interest whatever in her direction, which didn't please Ada. He was going out with a Physiotherapy student from the general hospital and was doing very nicely, thankyou. Judging from what he told us, he did most of the massage.

Despite the rugged Irishness of him, Seamus was a stickler for doing things correctly. He was neat and methodical and had the most beautiful pigskin case in which he kept his lecture notes and books. His father was an engraver back in Cork, and had engraved the letters S.H.D.T. on the case, these being his son's initials, although he had purposely dropped one of the names on his birth certificate and replaced it by another suitable one.

Seamus explained that his dad was very absent-minded and had to have someone to check his work before he sent it out. For instance, his baptismal name was really Seamus Henry Ignatius Toomey, but when his dad came to engrave the initials on his first school bag, poor Seamus was immediately sent home by the school teacher. After that, Ignatius was substituted by Dominic. It seemed that one of the nuns from the school nearly died from the horrors when she saw young Seamus walking into the school gates displaying the bag on his back for all to see.

But the most outstanding feature of our Irish friend was his feet. They were more like yards than feet, and he had to have his shoes especially made so that when we commenced

24

our course on appliance-making, a great and monumental problem arose.

In appliance-making, the foot is placed in a pan of plaster so that an impression is made which forms the mould for the eventual appliance. Here, again, we split into pairs and performed upon each other.

Alick teamed up with Seamus. When Seamus peeled off his socks, a great gasp arose from Alick.

"Boy, dem's some feet! Hallelujah!"

Poor Seamus's feet wouldn't fit in the pan. Other pans were sent for but to no avail. The cook, the gardener and even the boiler man were called in to help, with no more success.

"Yar feets too big," sang Alick in that calypso voice of his as he tried to force the Irishman's appendages into pan after pan without success. Twisting them and screwing them just didn't work.

"Yar feets too big - I love yer - but yar feets too big."

Finally, the truth had to be faced. There was not a pan in the building large enough.

"I'd kiss yar - yar feets too big . . . I'd hug yar, but yar feets too big."

Alick's voice could be heard all over the top floor of the school. But Stubbins soon put a stop to that and told Toomey to bring his own pan or tray or anything metal which his feet would fit into in time for the next session.

Now Seamus had an aunt living a few miles train journey from Barnfield and off he went to cadge a utensil for he had no money of his own. Aunt Philomena, so it seemed, worshipped the ground he trod on (a very large area I hasten to add) and would insist on obtaining the best tray she could find despite Seamus's protestations that any old thing would do. It was only for feet. But no, Aunt Philomena bought a beauty and when Seamus unwrapped it in front of the class a few days later, we saw a huge, shining tin dish.

"So you've got one, Toomey, I see," said Stubbins quite excitedly. "A cast of your foot - Podus Extraordinaire I'll call it - will add lustre to my collection. Your Celtic blood is, of course, the reason for my exhaustive research into the tribal origin of Enormous Extremities has proved that without any shadow of a doubt."

"Do you know what I'm going to tell you, Mister Stubbins. . ." began Seamus.

"Toomey, if I knew what you were going to tell me, then you wouldn't need to bother telling me, would you?" Stubbins

25

tittered mildly at his own joke.

"Living in England is bad enough, but I don't have to speak like the English, " retorted Seamus who, at times, became rather irritated by Stubbins's leg-pulling. ". . . But what I was going to say, sir, is that you're quite correct. We Toomeys are noted for our large extremities. "

"You is bragging again, Toomey! " sang out Alick.

"Quite enough of that, gentlemen. Remember there are ladies present. Now, kindly pass the pan over and also take off your shoes and stockings so we can get on with the job of making a cast of your Hibernian Protuberances. "

There was yet another titter from Mr Stubbins as he held the container up to his spectacles for closer inspection.

"If Galikeer's relatives had sent this over as a souvenir of his tribe's ancient customs - I indeed trust they are no longer in vogue, Galikeer - I would not have been surprised. "

"What do you mean by that, Mis'er Stubbins? "

"Only that I didn't know cannibalism was an Irish practice. . . " He peeled a printed notice off the tin which Seamus's aunty had omitted to remove. "It says here 'Baste well and cook slowly in a lowly heated oven'. . . but I think we will just content ourselves with making a cast of Toomey's Prize Winning Feet for posterity and take pot luck at the hospital canteen for lunch, as usual. Besides, some of us are Catholics and today is Friday. "

In common with every other profession, chiropody is saturated with folklore. For every do-it-yourself lawyer, there are hundreds of thousands of do-it-yourself chiropodists. And even the do-it-yourself doctors are outnumbered hundreds to one by D.I.Y. foot experts. No part of the human anatomy - not even the male skull - has come in for more home treatment than the foot. Even in these enlightened days patients often blithely inform the chiropodist, "Managed for years on me own, you know. Nothing to it really. But I can't bend like I used to do. It's me rheumatism, see? "

"Oh, I see all right, " says the chiropodist diplomatically.

"I don't see why there should be any training for such a job, " he is likely to be told. "After all, feet aren't like eyes, are they? I mean, eyes - well, they're real tricky with all them rods and cones and things. But feet! There's nothing to 'em. Just five toes and a sole and heel. Even if you give a week's study to each foot - and they can't call for more - that's only a fortnight. But they tell me you train for three years. No wonder the country's in the mess it is. All that time wasted! And all that money, too! "

26

Happily, the chiropodists are usually of a philosophical turn, and they parry all such remarks with a smile that can almost be described as amiable.

As Mr Stubbins had exploded one myth about the corn, I expected him to deal with that other just as explicitly - that is, the claim that a corn is a more reliable weather prophet than all the world's meteorologists put together.

To my surprise, and to the surprise of all the first-year students, he did no such thing. It was some time before we found out the reason, but when it finally came, it was as astounding as his pronouncement about the absence of roots from the common corn.

Stubbins, we were told, did sessional work at the Foot Hospital, as did most of the clinical and supervisory staff. Apparently, there was a certain Lydia Philpotts who under no circumstances would have her corn treated by anyone except Mr Stubbins. One never-to-be-forgotten day - July 12th, to be precise - she had rung in to say she would not be keeping her appointment, made for the following day.

"Surely you're not superstitious, Miss Philpotts?" Stubbins said.

"Superstitious?"

"Yes. Tomorrow is the thirteenth and it's a Friday."

"Oh, no, no, no!" Lydia protested. "That's not why I shall not be coming in."

"Then why not, may I ask?"

"Because, Mr Stubbins, it is going to be very wet tomorrow and I cannot make the journey in heavy rain."

Stubbins was astonished, for sunshine was flooding the valley, the air was saturated with bird song, and the sky was an unstained, almost hostile blue. Besides, the official forecast was a continuation of the fine and very warm weather for the next several days.

"You seem very sure that it will rain," said Stubbins. "How can you be so certain?"

"My corn, Mr Stubbins. It is announcing by painful semaphoring from my middle toe to my brain that large quantities of rain are on the way."

"Really!" exclaimed Stubbins, his tone not making it clear whether he was impressed by her gullibility or by her unquestioning confidence. Anxious to oblige one who was so devoted to him in his profession, he arranged another appointment.

"It must be a week today," said Miss Philpotts. "It's going to rain for at least six days."

As Stubbins put down the phone, his secretary heard him mutter, "If that woman ever married, her husband must have been called Noah. I've never heard such a flood of nonsense."

The next morning the sky was as black as if the sun had failed to rise. By ten o'clock the deluge had begun and it went on and on. Fields and roads disappeared, rivers overflowed their banks, houses and shops were in danger of vanishing under an ever-rising tide.

On the fifth day Miss Philpotts rang Mr Stubbins again. "What did I tell you?" she asked, her tone as triumphant as if she herself had caused the inundation. "And it will end tomorrow. The sun will shine again."

"I hope you're right," said Stubbins.

"I know I am," said Miss Philpotts.

And she was. The clouds rolled away on the sixth day and the sun shone with maximum splendour.

Mr Stubbins, always willing to be guided by experience, accepted that the corn Miss Philpotts sported did most certainly give warning of significant changes in the weather. And since then, science has given its own massively authoritative evidence to prove that the common foot corn is as reliable in weather forecasting as the most sophisticated meteorological equipment. According to the chemical analysis, a corn is composed of one substance - keratin. The nucleus of the corn is hydroscopic, or, in the parlance of the common layman, it absorbs moisture from the atmosphere, which impinges on the sensory nerves, thus causing pain. When the rain clouds move away, the pressure on the nerves is lifted and the pain disappears.

Not all corns give warning of changes in the weather. It is for this reason that many who claim to have meteorological corns prove woefully wrong in their forecasts of rain or shine. Farmers who keep corns for the double purpose of saving chiropody fees and being able to decide when to sow and to reap, may well be labouring under an illusion. Indeed, they might well be the victims of a misleading corn, so that they sow at the wrong time, and, in consequence, never reap at all. There are, in fact, cases on record of farmers plunging into bankruptcy and, at their public examinations, saying, "My corn let me down." Which explains why some liquidators have replied with some asperity, "You do not grow corn. You are a dairy farmer. I must advise you that it is a serious matter to try and deceive this court."

We were taken through the complexities of nail disorders from Onxchocryptosis (ingrown toe nail) to Onxchogryphosis or Ostler's toe, which is an overgrowth of nail, in the olden days often caused by horses standing on the ostler's foot. On one auspicious occasion, we were all summoned most enthusiastically to view an enormous nail on the foot of an ex-circus hand who claimed his foot had been stamped on by an elephant. Mr Stubbins claimed to have the best big toe nail collection in Britain and collected them like other men do butterflies or beer mats. Each one had a history and a case card containing over two hundred words.

"The one Vose is holding, " he announced one morning in the lecture room, "is one of the most unusual in my collection. It was four inches long from nailbed to its end which had embedded itself into the flesh of the patient's small toe. Hold it up, Vose. See the cavern-like part where it grew up from the flesh. "

I suddenly became aware of what it was I had in my hand and unfortunately I fumbled it and the nail dropped on the floor. Stubbins nearly had a heart attack.

"You got a weak stomach, Vose? Get down and find it man! "

Fortunately, after a lot of rooting and searching under the desks, I found it lodged under the radiator. What he'd have done if it had been damaged, I didn't dare to think for this was the prime piece of his collection. In fact, that toe nail had travelled the length and breadth of Britain on lecture tours which he undertook during his holidays. Indeed, the story went that he had made several unsuccessful attempts to insure it. Clive informed us that Mr Stubbins could trace a most serious misfortune to his devotion of feet. When I became one of his students, he lived in bachelor quarters, and I assumed he had never been married. Clive, as in so many other things, took the trouble to enlighten me.

"Oh, Stubbins has been married all right, " he said. "Well, more to the point, he married all wrong. "

"You mean he was mismated? " I asked.

"Not him. His wife. She had a great deal going for her. He first met her on holiday on the beach at Blackpool. She was sunbathing and wearing nothing but a very sketchy bikini. Nobody was surprised that Stubbins fell in love with her. "

"She must have been very beautiful, " I said.

"A genuine Aphrodite. Only she didn't rise from the foam; she lay on the sands, almost the whole of her in view, and Stubbins fell in love with her right away. "

"And she with him? "

"So it seems. In any case, after a very brief courtship,

they married. Now Nancy - for that was her name - had every reason - even every right - to believe that he had married her - all of her. "

"But he had, hadn't he? " I asked, puzzled.

"No, far from it. Nancy was sure he would love all of her. " Clive paused and sighed - almost as if he felt the poor girl's tragedy himself. "But no, " he continued, "not a bit of it. He gave all his attention to her feet. He looked at them, uttering exclamations of admiration. He stroked them, he fondled them, he kissed them. "

"You don't mean . . .? " I began.

"I do, " he said. "Nancy was quite happy that he should find so much pleasure in her feet. But she imagined that this was but the prelude to her husband transferring his attention to higher things. But no. His interest never rose any higher than her ankles, but, of course, it took Nancy some time to find that out. I understand that, on several occasions, she said, 'Percival, darling, there is more of me - much more. Just raise your eyes. There are hills and valleys, beautiful grazing grounds on which your lips and hands should linger. Don't stay for ever in the basement, to mix my metaphors. There are finer views from the drawing-room. As for what you will come upon in the bedroom, I just haven't the words to tell you'. "

"But all to no purpose? "

"To no purpose at all. She endured his foot worship for almost four months, but she could endure her frustration no longer. She left him. She walked out, leaving a note for him which read: 'I am leaving you to preserve my sanity. I bear you no malice as surely as I should never have borne you any children. Farewell. ' "

Clive went on to inform us that after his wife had run away Stubbins sold the house and moved into a flat, where he made one of the rooms into a Chiropody Museum. Clive had actually had the great honour of a private show. Viewing the 'Stubbins Collection' was the highest praise he could bestow upon a pupil. To be invited to his flat for 'tea and toenails', as it became known, was a feather in any student's cap. Alas, I never entered that sanctuary of Chiropodial Regalia to become one of the chosen few.

Chapter Three

Amongst the subjects we studied during the first year were Chemistry, Physics, Materia-Medica, Physiology and Biology. Much of this seemed to us to be no more than mental lumber, but the correctly-trained chiropodist is given a general knowledge of the make-up of the human body and of its origins and development. At first it seemed beyond me that learning how to turn red litmus paper blue could have anything to do with the common or garden British bunion, corn and callous.

Angela Lovelace was the biology teacher. A marvellous twenty-four and unmarried, she favoured excitingly short skirts and tantalisingly low--cut dresses.

"Teaches biology by example, by gum!" said Clive.

She did. Which explains why there was so much competition for students to occupy the front row. She must have used the most brittle chalk in existence. It broke several times during each lecture. The absolutely new student would dash to retrieve the broken piece. But only once. He would be subjected to such glares of disapproval only the most obtuse or incredibly bold would repeat the performance.

Angela, after glancing archly over her shoulder at the students, would go down for the chalk. And up would go her skirt, revealing ever more inches of the most exquisitely-shaped legs nature had ever moulded. When lecturing, she would bend over a student to explain a point he said he found obscure. While she explained a diagram or a passage from a textbook, the student would be giving rapt attention to the astonishing topography of her bosom. Solly Hymans gave her hell.

"Miss Lovelace," he once asked, "this matter of the reproductive processes of the guinea pig. You have told us that the young develop in the body of the female. But you have not told us how the life is triggered off in the female. Doesn't it have something to do with the male guinea pig?"

"Oh, a great deal," said Miss Lovelace uncertainly.

31

"Precisely what? "

"Well, the male makes love to the female. "

"Oh! " Hymans expressed immense surprise. "You mean they kiss and sort of coo? "

Miss Lovelace shook her lovely head and showed signs of embarrassment. "No, I don't think they do that. "

"But I thought that was making love. "

"Yes, it is among human beings and certain birds and other creatures. But there are some animals whose love-making is of a less refined nature. "

"You mean they dispense with the trimmings? Is that it, Miss Lovelace? But if they do that, just what is it they do? "

Miss Lovelace, by this time, was blushing. "Now that, " she hesitated, "is not easy to describe. Let me see now, how can I describe it? " She paused, hoping for inspiration, while the students waited, barely breathing, for what was to come next. "Yes, they would get together. "

This anti-climax produced a great sigh of disappointment from the students. But the crafty Hymans was by no means finished.

"But weren't they together before they made love, as you described it, Miss Lovelace? "

Then, just like many a boxer, she was saved by the bell.

"Time for lunch! " she announced in a high-pitched voice and bid a hasty retreat from the lecture room, her face bathed in perspiration.

Solly Hymans was rapidly establishing himself as the practical joker of our year and he didn't confine himself to embarrassing Miss Lovelace. Miss Hotchkiss soon discovered this trait in his character and had obviously marked him down as a young man to be carefully watched. The story of how he had pulled off a jape on me had got back to her and she had issued a severe reprimand to him in the privacy of her office and she was far from pleased when she realised that her entire staff, including Mr Stubbins, took it as a great joke. What had happened was this. Female patients removed their stockings in the privacy of cubicles which were curtained off one from the other. Solly had met a new patient in the entrance hall to the clinics. As she had never undergone chiropody treatment before she was somewhat baffled about the procedure prior to treatment. Solly ushered her into No. 4 cubicle and told her to remove her clothes. Though rather taken aback, she entered the cubicle and was further informed that a chiropodist would come for her when he was free. As soon as he saw my patient leaving the clinic, Solly came to me and told me that my next patient was waiting for me in No. 4 cubicle and asked me to go for her as she was new and rather shy. In my innocence I did what he requested and called to her that I was ready to attend to her feet.

"I'm in here, Doctor, " she answered.

I opened the curtains to see a middle-aged woman sitting on a chair clad only in a pair of panties and a red flannelette slip.

"Good heavens, Mrs Stirrup, I only want to see your feet! " I gasped in a fluster of utter embarrassment and pulled the curtains together so hastily that the end stopper came off the curtain rail.

"Oh! I'm sorry, " she cried in a high-pitched voice, "I thought you were being very thorough for a chiropodist. "

One of the highlights of our clinical duties was to accompany Professor Potter on his Clinic Rounds. He paid us a visit from the General Hospital to hold a varicose vein clinic and one hour was given over to this on the first Friday of every month. Selected patients were seated on the high treatment chairs and the professor would go from one to the other, giving his verdict on the veins in question. He was always accompanied by a nurse, who would make notes as he gave his diagnosis and proposed treatment. For some it would be elastic stockings, for others an operation would be advised. He had a marvellous bed-side manner and always put the patient at ease. But to the students he was the best entertainment possible for he was a noted eccentric and must have been the original absent-minded professor; and was known affectionately as 'potty Potter'. The old boy was a bachelor and far too involved with the two great loves of his life - training pet monkeys to perform tricks and varicose veins - to be concerned about his personal appearance. Sometimes he would arrive in a suit which looked as if he had slept in it for a month and regularly wore odd socks. Prior to meeting this esteemed gentleman in the flesh, I had only ever seen Will Hay portray the bungling, incompetent professor on the screen. Not that 'Potty' was incompetent, he was, in fact, a brilliant and esteemed specialist, but he was such a source of amusement that he attracted a large crowd of students and hangers-on, who were just as keen to have a laugh as they were to take in the knowledge he imparted. It was not unusual for him to pause in the middle of his diagnosis and gaze out of a window, as if he had forgotten all about the patient and the audience. Then, suddenly realising where he was, he would ask the tutor to tell him what he had said previously. But

C

33

most memorable of all Potty's meandering rounds brought the entire proceedings down to the level of a college pantomime.

He was closely examining the skin on the legs of a middle-aged woman and mumbling to himself, as if unaware of the eager eyes watching his every move. Suddenly, in a loud voice, he announced:

"Dermatitis, gentlemen. A post menopausal condition undoubtedly," and then, passing on to the next pair of legs displayed on the chair rests, he said, "Snap! Here we have another exact condition." There was a great roar of laughter. Even Miss Hotchkiss joined in the mirth. The professor looked up over his spectacles, somewhat surprised, to see a man of well over seventy years of age looking extremely mystified.

Practical experience was to be had in abundance. Occasionally the local doctors near the hospital would refer patients for chiropody treatment. One case stays in my mind vividly. A middle-aged Irishman came in one evening in overalls. He was employed on a local building site and had a note from his G.P. which said that he complained of great pain in the Plantar Metatarsal area of his left foot, but try as he may he could not find any reason for this pain or for the indentation in that region. One of the clinicians examined the foot with me. There was no sign of inflammation, just a groove. Obviously, we thought, he must have some obstruction in his boot. On examination we found that the boot was perfectly flat inside and he assured us that his other shoes were perfectly smooth. Yet the pain was so severe at times that he had to sit down on the job. We were baffled. The clinician went off to seek the advice of that fountain of foot knowledge, Mr Stubbins. I picked up the patient's socks and examined them at arm's length while waiting for Mr Stubbins.

"How often do you change them?" I asked the patient.

"I lives on me own, sir," said he, "and I leaves 'em on a while, sir. Don't you know, it saves the washing costs, sir."

On closer examination and at the risk of dying from asphyxiatión, I found that two socks were matted together and must have been like that for months, and then I felt a lump. On peeling the socks apart, between them I found an old-fashioned back collar stud. The case was solved. Sherlock Holmes couldn't have felt prouder than I did.

"Here's the cause of your trouble," I said, holding up the stud triumphantly.

"Be-dad, I wondered where the bloody thing had got to - ye're a gintleman and a clever doctor, sir . . . good luck to ye!"

34

He agreed to let me keep the stud and I presented it to Stubbins for his celebrated collection. This somewhat compensated for the faux pas over my careless operating on a postman's foot, and I felt Stubbins saw me now in a better light. However, I found that though there was no vindictiveness in his make-up, he dearly loved to have a laugh at a student's expense if possible. The first time I fell victim to his wit was over the very first exam paper we took. This was a mock exam after three months, set with a view to finding out just how much notice we were taking of his lectures.

". . .And now, Vose, " He adjusted his pince-nez and flickered his eyes on the paper in front of his nose. ". . .Not a bad effort, I suppose. Shows promise, but do remember, Vose, that a person who bleeds copiously when cut is Haemophiliac and not a Nymphomaniac. I can see you being sued for damages one day if you don't make a mental note. I must add, purely from a clinical observation, that both are, unfortunately rare. " Not satisfied at getting the best laugh of the week out of my monumental clanger, he exposed me to further banter the following week. For three months I had harboured a closely-guarded secret. As far as I knew, only Miss Hotchkiss and her secretary knew about it because it had come out in answers to questions at the interview. Several of the students had done military service and some had decided to take up chiropody after being in the medical corp. as orderlies. "Let me see now, " Stubbins said, "how many of you had medical experience in the forces? " Six hands went up. "Of course you were Grade 3, were you not, Vose? What was it now? I have it on the record cards in the office. "

There was a deadly silence. My dad had always said 'Tell the truth and shame the Devil'. With a gulp, I blurted out, "Flat feet, sir. "

"Ah, yes that's it! " said Stubbins amidst the laughter.

Ever after I was known as 'Flat Foot Vose'.

Back at the digs, things were going from bad to worse. When the first-year lads had first taken up residence, Ada always served the meals. Most of us worked in our bedrooms after the evening meal. Ada was crafty. She'd watch for who left the house and when she knew there was a student in a room alone, she'd come up and knock on the door. I'd been there about six months when I got my first knock.

"Hello, who is it? " I called out.

"It's Ada, John - Ada Crabshaw. "

"Can I help you? " I raced across the floor and slipped the bolt into place. This was the first time she had used my

35

Christian name.

"It's me feet - me arches. They dropped when I was out shopping."

I had the most illuminating mental picture of a huge crash in the high street.

"I'm sorry to hear that, Ada. Hope they'll soon be better." I tried to sound sympathetically disinterested.

"Can you look at them, please?" she sounded desperate.

Now, I didn't want to be downright rude, so I opened the door ever so slightly.

"Will you look at them for me?" she asked again.

She tried to enter and in the aperture I saw her big toe waggling. I had heard tell of so-called sexy feet but, as far as I was concerned, she couldn't have exhibited anything more guaranteed to discourage any notions lurking in my bosom towards her than her big toe.

"Well . . . you see . . . I mean I'm not a chiropodist yet. I've only been here six months - get the doctor."

"But they don't do feet. Maybe you'd learn a bit if I came in."

She could say that again, but the knowledge I was likely to accumulate would be of no value in my exams.

"No, Ada. I'm sorry - go to the doctor or go over the road to the clinic."

I gently closed the door and she was forced to remove her foot.

She tried us all in turn. It was when she realised there was nothing doing that she started to get nasty. She didn't serve the food any more. She almost threw it at us and was constantly rowing with her mother so that some evenings we were lucky to get a meal at all.

Then one night Mrs Crabshaw broke down in tears all over the sandwiches she'd brought in for our supper. Ada had run off with a Maori tribesman who was studying medicine at the university. She'd warned her not to speak to strange men but she'd gone over to him in the Labour Club one evening and the next thing she knew, Ada had packed her bags and was living with him in sin.

"Heaven forbid. She'll end up the grandmother of illegitimate Chinese grandchildren," she sobbed.

Her geography was as bad as her cooking.

To hear her talk, poor Ada was ruined. And even if he did the decent thing and married her, she'd be marrying into a lot of heathens. Mrs Crabshaw began to go down the nick, her nerves were shattered and she started to give us hell as well

36

as potatoes.

The place just got shabbier and shabbier and the food more horrible than ever. Some nights there was nothing at all under the piles of spud, and the breakfasts were burned more often than not. Most of my spending money was going on indigestion powder and bicarbonate of soda. She was hitting the bottle and we were the victims of it all. She was too mean to get help or have the place decorated. The house couldn't have been decorated for at least thirty years. Clive swore that the letters E.M. on his bedroom wall stood for Emily Pankhurst and not Ernest Pike, a past lodger. Rising damp had won hands down.

One evening I made the statement that I was sure she served the eggs left over from the evening meal for breakfast the following morning. The idea of the piled spuds was that we'd be so fed up we wouldn't eat what lay below. The rest of the lads didn't believe this, but I was certain in my own mind for I recognised the eggs when they came back the next day.

I decided to try out my theory. The next evening I brought back a bottle of gentian violet from the clinic; also an orange stick. After disposing of the nightly dose of potatoes, I dipped the orange stick into the dye then stuck it into the white of the egg.

The next morning we waited with baited breath for the breakfast to be served. Sure enough the violet-stained egg turned up on Clive's plate. I had to eat it but I took a tanner off each of them which made it worthwhile.

I'd won my bet and that was the straw which broke the camel's back. We'd had enough. Surely there were better digs in Gadsbury? The local Sally Army could do better than that. In fact, we gave the matter considerable thought. We'd put many a bob in the collecting box at the 'Bull and Trumpet', and Solly had a pile of 'War Crys' propping up the dicky leg on his side of the bed, which groaned and moaned throughout the night under his great carcase.

At last, after three weeks of searching, we found a place two roads away. It was clean and the owners seemed very nice. But who was going to break the news to Mrs Crabshaw? Ten of us were going to hand in our notices. Who would be first? We called an extraordinary meeting in the snug room of the 'Bull and Trumpet' and decided the only fair way was to draw lots. Clive drew the first one, I drew the last one. Poor old Clive, I thought, but how wrong can you be! Things had reached such a state that she no longer served the food. We had to go to the kitchen for it ourselves. I felt sorry for Clive as he went off for his plate. He returned smiling, I was soon to

37

find out how wrong I was. By the time I got there, she had already lost nine times five pounds in one fell swoop, and I received the sopping wet dish cloth full in my face. We packed our bags and took them across to the new digs.

Poor old Alick, who, in my opinion, was progressing at the practical side better than any of us, drew many a sour look from the patients as they sat in the chair ready to be treated by a black man. This was before the days of the influx of coloured people into the medical profession in England, and they looked upon him as some kind of witch doctor capable of putting a spell on their feet and crippling them for life.

We became familiar with the legendary remarks so well-known to the practising chiropodist.

"When your feet hurt, you hurt all over, " must take pride of place. This is usually accompanied by a belly chuckle, as if the patient is under the impression that it's an original gag. Some folks will repeat it as many as six times during a treatment and drive you to the point of screaming.

"They only hurt when I stand on 'em, " is another. Solly became so infuriated by one woman with a high-pitched voice who kept repeating this that he put his scalpel down and said,

"If you sat down, Madam, maybe you would get the pain somewhere else. "

Sure enough, later in the morning, he was up before Miss Hotchkiss for gross insolence to a patient and received a severe reprimand.

"Do I need to take me shoes and socks off, luv? " is another old chestnut, which, of course, inevitably brought the obvious answer:

"It'll be a lot easier on my scalpel if you do, Missus. "

"I've come with me feet, Mister, " one old dear said to me one day.

Stubbins was within earshot and remarked in a loud voice,

"I trust you take them home with you as well, Madam."

On another occasion, I was treating a most fussy, fidgety patient who would persist in slapping her knees every now and then with her hands, so that I had to keep one eye on them and one on her foot, which was becoming something of a strain. This was made even worse by her insistence on bending down to push her fingers between her toes to indicate where her various corns were situated. She was the epitome of the nervous patient. Several times I asked her politely to desist, but to no avail. In the end I adopted a sterner manner. "Please Mrs King, for your own sake, don't fiddle with your toes while

38

I am operating on them."

"I'm not fiddling with them, young man, I'm counting them," she replied.

It was about this time, shortly before our change of digs, that we were indoctrinated with the folk lore and fact of that wart of the foot - the Verruca. I repeat, the word is VERRUCA and not FAROUKA as many people call it. Not in any way is it an Egyptian disease or peculiar to the feet of oil sheiks. There is such an aura of mystery surrounding it that some patients speak about it in hushed whispers.

A Verruca Pedis, to give is its full title, is simply a wart of the foot. It is a virus and mainly found on the feet of children and young people, due to contagion by communal living, swimming baths and athletic changing rooms. And it can be the devil's own job to cure. In fact, unless electrolysis and fulguration, or surgery, are used, no chiropodist can truthfully say he can cure a verruca. There are dozens of different treatments all of which we were taken through by Stubbins but the most amazing revelation was that he actually gave credence to the old antiquity steeped yarns about remedies of curing warts. But, of course, he put such cures down to the 'psychological factor' and pooh-poohed the idea that the old professional wart charmers had any value in themselves.

Many rituals were performed on the advice of these wart charmers. One popular one was for the patient to stand in front of an ash tree and address it in these words:

'Ash tree, Ash tree,
Pray, buy these warts from me.'

The patient then stuck a long pin into the said tree, withdrew it, then, biting hard on the teeth, stuck it into the wart. It was then extracted from the wart and replaced in the tree where it was left to go rusty. If the patient carefully followed the charmer's instructions, it was claimed that the wart would go away completely. Some chiropodists used to purchase the wart from the patient for a penny each. This worked especially well with children. This 'buying of the wart' as it became known, produced some of the most amazing cures.

Burying steak in the garden is another trick and as the steak rots, so does the wart. Bird lime from the female rook applied twice daily and covered with wet newspaper is another old favourite. Mind you, devotees of this one claim that reading a passage from the Rubaiyat of Omar Khayyam before applying the newspaper, speeds up the process somewhat.

Legend has it that in days of old, a witch from Oswaldtwistle used to bite them off for the price of a milk stout and the last recorded mention of her was that she was rotting in Lancaster gaol awaiting trial for witchcraft. But the wart and witchcraft are synonymous.

Now Solly suffered with verrucae quite badly and, try as the clinicians might, they could not remove them completely. He reckoned he'd picked them up from a little Jewish tailor, which was just as well for we'd never have heard the end of it if he'd been a Catholic or a member of the Church of England. Mind you, I was firmly convinced that they were not warts at all but an outcrop of Brewer's rash or some such alcoholic disease. Solly was desperate. One day, he announced in the digs during tea that he was going to try an old charmer's remedy. I prayed to heaven that it wasn't the 'bird lime of female rook' routine, for don't forget I had to sleep with him. But no, he'd come up with another one which none of us had heard about. A great aunt who once had a sideshow on New Brighton pier had sent it to him, written out in great detail on the back of a whist card:

'Take one stiff black cat (dead) and place in a bag. Seal bag. Take bag, accompanied by at least two male accomplices (Christians will suffice) to the cemetery at midnight. As the church clock strikes the bewitching hour, whirl the bag round the head six times then hurl it as far as possible before the clock has finished striking. Return home and on awakening in the morning, the wart will have vanished completely. '

I told him quite bluntly that he was a fool to believe such rubbish and to make an appointment at the hospital to have them removed surgically.

But Seamus Toomey thought the idea was great.

"Sure and aren't we chiropodists? It's the very chance to try out these old tales. So it is. When I'm after me tea, I'll nip down the backs and go through the middens. There's dozens of moggies around here. "

There was no putting him off the idea and sure enough half an hour later, he came back complete with stiff black cat in a bag which he had securely tied with brown string. We stayed up late that night swotting our anatomy while awaiting the bewitching hour. The cemetery was only two minutes down the road so at exactly five minutes to twelve, we set out for Gadsbury graveyard. The moon shone eerily upon the gravestones as we tiptoed cautiously across the grass to a wide space ideal for the casting off of missiles. A feeling of imminent doom engulfed me but it was too late to back out. Seconds seemed like an eternity. Then with a spine-chilling stridency the clock

40

struck One . . . Two . . . Solly began to whirl the wart curing device round his huge shoulders - six times he did it and, exactly as Aunt Rubena had ordered, let fly before the clock struck the last of its strident notes.

All went deadly quiet - for about ten seconds that is - then a terrific crash of splintering glass shattered the mystic tranquility of the cemetery. I had an urgent desire to visit the toilet.

"What the bloody 'ell are you playin' at? " was the next sound we heard. There was nothing mysterious about the voice, it was broad Yorkshire and very angry.

But we were hell bent for the main gates by then. When we got there, they were locked. The lodge keeper must have nipped round and closed them on the stroke of the hour. Solly was far too fat to squeeze through the railings and so we had to push him up a tree so that he could drop from a branch into the road. I saw his skull cap fall off when he bounced on the pavement, but I was far too frightened to stop and pick it up.

That night the three of us lay in our beds in trepidation, expecting at any time to hear the heavy feet of the law crunching the gravel of the path. But at last Morpheus, in his great mercy, engulfed us with his soothing balm and in the morning we awoke refreshed and confident that we had not been discovered.

Solly stuck his flabby foot on my knee as I sat on the bed wiping the sleep from my eyes.

"Has it gone? " he enquired anxiously.

I had to break the sad news to him that Aunt Rubena's charm hadn't worked. In fact, the warts seemed larger than ever.

Before lectures began that morning, Mr Stubbins came into the common room and announced:

"Toomey, Vose and Hymans are required to report to Miss Hotchkiss's office immediately. "

My God, we'd been tumbled!

In the office we found a police constable and two men, one of whom was a stranger to us, but the other was the owner of the house next to Mrs Crabshaw's and the biggest nosey-parker in the district, and noted for peeping at the courting couples who gathered under the trees by the foot hospital railings.

On Miss Hotchkiss's table was a black bag tied with brown string. Next to it was Solly's skull cap. She was at her iciest.

"It has been brought to my notice by Constable Jones that the three of you caused damage to Mr Blackler's greenhouse. "

she began. "F-five pounds worth of damage has been done by this . . . m-missile . . . or whatever it is."

She pulled a face and I wondered if she had got a whiff of its contents.

"Do you deny you are responsible?" she demanded, edging away.

Solly stood up, then sat down again, not sure what to say.

"Because Mr Highfield, who lives next door to your accommodation, says that he saw the three of you sneaking into the cemetery at midnight as he took his dog for a walk. Is that not so, Mr Highfield?"

The man smirked and nodded, gloating inwardly at the awful fate he hoped we'd get for he hated the students who, he claimed, lowered the tone of the district.

Give Solly his due, he owned up. Mind you, he'd not much choice. Everyone in Gadsbury knew that skull cap.

"It is entirely my fault, Miss Hotchkiss," he said. "I threw the bag. These other fellows simply came with me. I apologise to Mr Blackler here but I didn't do it deliberately and I will pay the five pounds back to him, or at least my father will."

Miss Hotchkiss looked at Mr Blackler, Mr Blackler looked at the P.C. Miss Hotchkiss was worried stiff it would get in the papers, of course. She, in turn, looked hard at Solly.

"Well . . . w-why were you in the cemetery, Hymans? Why did you throw this . . . this . . . object?"

All the time she was gradually moving further away from it. The smell of the pickled foot in the formalin jar had nothing on this beauty.

"To cure my veruccae, Miss Hotchkiss," said Solly bravely.

The P.C. coughed loudly and Mr Blackler looked hard at his boots. Miss Hotchkiss stuttered incoherently for a few seconds, then became silent. Solly then told the whole tale, blow by blow. Mr Blackler was a decent chap and saw the joke and promised not to press charges as long as he got his five pounds.

Mr Highfield was obviously disgusted and left without saying good morning. We got a good rollocking and told that we were on our last warning. Finally, she made Solly swear he'd throw the cause of all the bother in the incinerator.

Seamus couldn't wait to carry out the instruction for the burning of the bag, and ran off down the back stairs into the garden with Solly hard on his heels. The incinerator door was jammed and Toomey was trapped.

"Open the bag, " ordered Solly, his huge arms open ready to squeeze the Irishman into a pulp.

He obviously considered the Irishman's extreme haste to be very suspicious.

"Don't be an eejut. Do youse want us to get the bloody plague? " said Seamus, doing his best to prise open the iron door.

But Solly had a penknife and had the bag undone before Seamus could do anything about it. He let it drop to the ground and out popped the head of a white cat. Seamus knew what would happen next. Words were not required and he took off like an olympic sprinter, but he'd hardly reached the sanctuary of the bicycle shed when the bag caught him full in the back of the neck. It was weeks before Solly forgave him for not carrying out Aunt Rubena's orders to the letter, for it is well-known amongst disciples of the charm cures that to make a mockery of them can produce disastrous results.

The following Thursday, Solly was given the afternoon off to have his veruccae surgically removed though his faith in charms didn't wane. He was convinced that a black cat would have done the trick.

Chapter Four

Christmas was approaching, and it seemed that the previous year's party was one of gloomy memory. So Miss Hotchkiss asked the students to organise the next one. As I had always fancied myself with a pen I set about writing a sketch. Unhappily, it had a rehearsal in the wrong place at the wrong time. About a fortnight before the party, Stubbins was lecturing us on Pes Planus or flat foot. I was too immersed in putting finishing touches to the sketch to be taking the least notice. Unfortunately, engrossed though he was in his lecture, Stubbins noticed me.

"Mr Vose!"

I jerked to instant attention. "Sir!"

"I am delighted to see you taking such copious notes. I have never known you write so industriously. I am indeed gratified. You are setting your fellow students a most excellent example." He beamed benignly. "I shall be obliged if you will read out what you have written. I am sure it will be most enlightening."

"We-ell, sir," I stammered. "If you will excuse me, I would rather. . ."

"Oh, come, Vose," he interrupted. "Your modesty is most commendable, but you must not deprive us of the help you can give."

I looked at the unfinished sketch, but the words I needed to utter refused to pass my throat.

Stubbins came over to me, hand outstretched. "I will read the notes for you," he said. "That may save your blushes a little."

Most unwillingly I handed the pages over. As Stubbins read what I had written, my face became very red indeed. In a tone of the most silky manner which made the script sound even worse than it was, he proclaimed:

"VOSE: I say, I say, Toomey, old boy. Did you know 'Pilgrim's Progress' is Mr Stubbins's favourite

44

book?

TOOMEY: No, I didn't, Vose. Why is it his favourite book?

VOSE: Because it was written by John Bunyan - Oi! . . "

There was the kind of silence that follows upon the announcement of a declaration of war along with an outbreak of typhoid. Smiling seraphically, Stubbins continued:

"TOOMEY: I'm after asking you, Vose, what did the Irishman say to the chiropodist?

VOSE: I don't know, Toomey. What did the Irishman say to the chiropodist?

TOOMEY: Me fates in your hands - Oi!

VOSE: M O N O L O G U E : She was only a chiropodist's daughter, But my! Was she good under the arches! "

The atmosphere in a morgue when it is overcrowded is far happier than the atmosphere was in that lecture hall. Stubbins went on relentlessly.

"VOSE: What is the most common foot complaint in Dublin?

TOOMEY: I don't know, Vose. What is the most common foot complaint in Dublin?

VOSE: Lepra-corns - Oi!

TOOMEY: Oh, don't be callous!

VOSE: How about a song?

TOOMEY: A good idea. The chiropodists national anthem should go down well.

VOSE: What's that?

TOOMEY: Toot Toot Tootsie Goodbye! "

The Black Death might have broken out all over again as he ceased reading.

"May I ask what this is? " he asked.

"It's a script for the Christmas party, sir. It's the rehearsal tonight. "

"And you are expecting this to make us feel merry? "

"We-ell-er . . . I . . . that is . . . "

"Vose.' I cannot imagine anything more likely to kill the spirit of Christmas than this depresing effusion. I am fond of both punning and feet, but the two together could be rather nauseating to say the least. "

"It's entitled 'Chiropodial Capers', sir, " I pointed out. "It's meant to be corny - if you'll excuse the pun, sir. "

"It's corny all right. Did it occur to you that the last

people in the world to want a corny Christmas must be chiropodists?" As he spoke he was tearing up the script. "I might
add," he said, "that if this is a sample of your humour, I
thank God that, on the night of the party, I shall be attending
a lecture of 'The Importance of Elastic Hosiery in Modern
Society'."

"That's stretching it a bit, isn't it?" I said. "Missing
the party, I mean."

I swear that no pun was intended. I had said it before I
realised the connection.

"Vose," said Stubbins, "for a certainty, you are severely
stretching my patience. I can only say that you will never,
never make me laugh. If you do anything, you will make me
weep." He gestured towards the door. "The class is dismissed, but before we do depart, Toomey, I would have thought
that Toot Toot Tootsie Goodbye was the anthem of your patients
by the groans escaping from Room No. 5 Clinic this morning?"

Over dinner that evening, Clive said, "Are you taking up
the challenge, John?"

When I looked blank, he went on.

"Stubbins's challenge? He said you would never make him
laugh - remember?"

"That wasn't a challenge," I said.

"Oh, but it was. And if it wasn't, this is." He took a note
from his wallet. "I'll bet you a pound you don't make him
laugh in the next four weeks."

I hesitated. "He does laugh easily," I said.

"Then you're on to a good thing," said Clive, waving the
note enticingly in front of my face.

"You wouldn't be risking a pound if you thought I was.
However. . ." I reached into my pocket. "The bet's on."

"'Tis giving it away," said Seamus.

"Man," said Alick, "is you Midas or something?"

I felt I was an idiot. I had acted rashly in rising to Clive's
bait. In those days a quid was money - real money - commanding sixteen pints of beer, or one hundred cigarettes. And I
had virtually thrown all that wealth away.

My chance came sooner than I anticipated. In fact, it came
the very next day. We were all busy in the clinic when Stubbins
said to the patients, "Ladies and gentlemen, I trust you will
excuse us for a few minutes. But a most interesting case has
just come in and I would like the students to see it." We all
gathered around.

A man wearing a Tam o'Shanter and a kilt was sitting in
a high chair, his left foot on a rest. The sight itself was

46

amusing.

"This gentleman, " Stubbins explained to the assembly of students, "has come here in great pain. The case is more in the field of the general hospital, but before I send him there for treatment I would like you to look closely at the afflicted foot. Kindly remove your other shoe and stocking, Mr McKay, " requested Stubbins.

"Och . . . it's no me other foot, mister . . . there's nae mooch wrong wi' that only a wee corn. "

"I wish to compare your feet, Mr McKay, if you will kindly oblige. "

"I tell you, there's nae the marter wi' it . . . dinna waste yer time. It's precious tae ye. "

"Please, Mr McKay. Kindly take your other shoe and stocking off! "

Stubbins was getting impatient.

The man grumbled and mumbled as he peeled off his green stocking and high-heeled brogue.

"Dinna blame me . . . I didna knae ye'd want to see ma left foot. "

We soon realised the cause of his obstinacy. His left foot was black. He had only washed his right one!

"The neglect of personal hygiene is one of the predisposing factors to infection, " said Stubbins sarcastically. "This gives us a clue as to why the foot became infected. " Close to the ankle was a huge lump, its angry red colour showing that it had turned septic. After we had all looked at the protuberance for some time, Stubbins turned to me.

"Vose, " he said, "kindly give me your diagnosis. "

It was clear that the foot was badly infected. "Are you in pain, Mr McKay? " I enquired.

"I canna begin t'tell ye. I canna sleep for the swine. "

I gingerly felt the surrounding tissues, which were hot.

"I gather from the symptoms, " I said, "that the patient has a badly infected lesion on the dorsal surface due to injury."

"Aye, man, ye're reet aboot that, " said McKay. "I dropped a brick on it. "

"Just as I thought. " I felt a surge of satisfaction at being proved right. "Note the layer of newly-formed granulation tissue or abscess. The lesion also has all the classic signs of inflammation, namely heat, redness, pain and impairment of function - or, in Latin - Calor, Rubor, Tumor . . ."

"We'll be glad to settle for the English version, Vose, thank you, " Stubbins interrupted. "And what is your conclusion? "

47

"An operable lesion requiring after-treatment with a course of antibiotics. I also notice that, according to Mr McKay's notes, he is a diabetic having daily Insulin. His condition, naturally, is even more alarming due to the diabetes being a pre-disposing cause to the spread of infection."

"Well done, Vose. . .By the way, Mr McKay," said Stubbins, "which part of Scotland are you from?"

"Frae the Sutherlands, sir - a wee place by the name of Kinlockdervie."

This was my golden chance and I grabbed it eagerly.

"Then, sir," I said, suddenly inspired, "I'd say you are suffering from a Highland Gathering."

Stubbins laughed. So did everybody else, with one exception. As Clive handed me his pound note he wasn't even smiling.

The first-year examinations came and most of us passed. It was then that we learnt that success can often be more destructive than failure. Most of us, including myself, decided we could rest on our laurels. I felt this way even though the second year was much tougher than the first. Anatomy was still baffling me. And temptation was beginning to raise its entrancing, bewitching head. To the allurements of the pint and dominoes was added the enticements of midweek football and race meetings.

We went to watch Everton when we should have been at the hospital watching demonstrations of foot treatment. We were at Haydock Park watching our four-footed friends losing as if they were our sworn enemies. At the same time we were missing vital lectures that were necessary if we were to pass our exams.

The results of all this misguided behaviour became apparent when we took another mock exam. The results were pathetic. After Miss Hotchkiss had rounded us up in her office and blasted us for missing lectures and demonstrations, she passed us on to Stubbins. He knew jolly well we had not been working. We were called in to the lecture room ten minutes before the usual starting time to be told in no uncertain terms how we stood.

"Though I do not subscribe to the gutter press, gentlemen, I do read the local papers and I am fully aware that the 'Bull and Trumpet' dominoes team are having their best season ever. A proficiency at pub games is a sign of a misspent youth, and in the case of several of you misspent time as chiropody students. Football is another curse - it interferes with study and it has lately been brought to our notice that some of the pupils have been missing lectures to attend matches. When I was a student, everyone in my year was studious. Football and similar distractions went by the board. Work is the only way to get on in life. There is no success without it. . ."

Solly was trying his best to hold back an alcoholic yawn but it escaped in a sort of muted groan.

"Yes, Hymans, W-O-R-K - work. You know the word? You have heard of it? It is the one four-letter word which appears to be missing from your vocabulary, Hymans. It has its root derivatives in the Siberian salt mines and the skeletons of the Israelites who carried the hods on the pyramid contract. Its practical application gave birth to such words as blood, sweat, toil and tears and its very mention is guaranteed to reduce any Labour Exchange queue in the world. It strikes me that the majority of this class are frightened of the word. But without it your future is blank. The results of the mock exam are probably the poorest we have ever had and yet most of you have good academic backgrounds, which, in a nutshell, means you are bone idle. There is nothing worse than a student who has the brains but won't use them. It is sacrilege. Unless a better standard of work is produced in the next exam, then severe methods will be used. We have plenty of applicants for this course, so don't think you can stay here and do nothing. Believe me, your future is in your own hands and I would advise you to change your ways dramatically. Anyone, in future, who misses lectures or clinical work without a legitimate reason will be suspended for two weeks and upon a further transgression will be expelled."

Even though this threat seemed to be a purposely concocted one to frighten us, there was no doubting Stubby was very annoyed. We had taken advantage of his good nature and it hurt him.

This tirade, nevertheless, did have results. The minibus man lost a lot of custom and the sales at the pub must have fallen off considerably for a while. The dominoes team started to fade and Jack Quinn, the publican, was very cross. Still, I preferred Jack's anger any day to Stubbins's and so I became more industrious in my studies. Solly, of course, had always swotted in the domino room of the pub, so he didn't see any reason to alter his method. He simply went in an hour earlier.

But temptation, that elfish pricker of man's weakness, was nodding its attractive head in the clinics. We were into our second year now and, with hundreds of hours of practical work behind us, were quite competent operators. The appointment system was such that patients could only attend every two months. Some had such bad feet that this was too long. It was an Irishman who first dangled the bait.

He was sitting in a chair with his shoes off. One sock was yellow, the other white.

"You've got odd socks on, Mr Kelly, " I remarked.

"Sure, I've got another pair at home the same, " he said, without batting an eyelid, then proceeded to look around in a furtive fashion.

"Do youse do foreigners, son? " he asked in a hissing whisper.

"We do anyone, Mr Kelly. " I replied in my normal voice.

He waved me down to a whisper.

"Shush. No, I don't mean that. I mean do youse do it on the side. In the evenings? The wife's feet are bad and her nails are ripping me to pieces in bed, so they are. "

I told Satan to get behind me. But he didn't.

"See you outside, " I whispered.

I took Mrs Kelly on as a private patient, also the mother-in-law, who was ninety-seven, and the woman next door who used to be a wrestler and had stubbed her big toes on her opponent's posterior so often the nails were crumbling and filling the bed full of bits so badly that they were getting into her husband's pyjama bottoms, so said Mr Kelly. Three patients! I was elated. The possibilities were endless.

That very night I set out for the Kelly household, but I couldn't shake off the pangs of conscience. But I needed the money. There I was on Mother Kelly's doorstep ready to operate on Mother Kelly's instep. Should I bang the knocker? A wave of guilt engulfed me as I held it. I began to wish I had stayed at the digs swotting. Should I? I did and four other doors opened. It was one of those terraced streets with no gap between the houses for the entire length of the street. A woman next door in mob cap and curlers, called out to me.

"Hello, luv. You're from foot clinic, aren't you? Thought as I knew you. Never had them done so good in my life, luv . . knock harder. They're probably watching Coronation Street. Go on, luv, knock harder! Have you had no tea? "

I was sorely tempted to take flight. Two more doors across the street opened, and another woman's voice shouted:

"Aye . . . tap on winder, young man. They'll come. Gas-man always does that. Does he do privates, Maggie? " This last question was shouted to the woman who had first spoken.

"No, only feet, Alice, " came the reply.

"I mean that, you daft devil! "

Such a cackling was set up at this last remark that the woman who had asked the question slammed the door in a fit of pique. This was the signal for at least six more doors to open.

I was rapidly becoming a street curiosity. Fortunately Mrs Kelly opened her door. I treated the three patients, including the lady wrestler who had the biggest feet I'd ever seen, man or woman, her ankles bulbous with veins through many years of Boston crabs and two falls or one submission.

Once outside, I turned a deaf ear to the old woman next door's pleas for me to come and do her sometime and away I ran down the street. If I kept on like this I'd be out on my ear. My stupid conscience just wouldn't let me feel happy. Just then a red car came round the corner and I recognised Mrs Bradshaw, the secretary of the school. I pressed myself into a doorway and, as luck would have it, she didn't see me. She was Miss Hotchkiss's chief informant and seeing me carrying a case would have had her spilling the beans the next day to old Hotch. Feeling more like a secret abortionist than a chiropodist, I sneaked down the back alleys with my black bag and, because I was shaking so much, spent some of the fifteen bob I'd made on a couple of whiskies at the Labour Club. I just hadn't got the stomach for illicit practice, even though I knew it was a common enough method of making pocket money with other students.

Seamus Toomey was made of much sterner stuff. Not for him to duck and hide, already he was in business for himself and getting into the habit of missing lectures. In fact, he missed whole days and was constantly having to make excuses, but we all knew he couldn't get away with it for very long. It was simply a matter of time and the strange thing was that everyone seemed to know except Seamus himself. He had various things going for him, the most lucrative was massaging the local football team reserves, a job he had landed by convincing the trainer he was a qualified masseur. His girlfriend, the physiotherapy student, had given him a few lessons and, armed with this little knowledge and bags of confidence and natural charm, he was earning several quid a week. Besides this, he did 'foreigners' and had built up quite a large clientele of chiropody patients, but the most bare-faced enterprise was the selling of corn plasters and footpaste to the customers; products deeply frowned upon by Stubbins so Seamus couldn't have picked a more precarious graft. All of a sudden he had become extremely courteous and obliging to the patients. He would put the ladies' nylons on and make a real fuss as he escorted them out of the door. It was in the hallway that his sales drive started and he would pull out his samples from a case which he kept hidden away behind the coat rack. Arch supports, toe separators, cuticle removers; but to my mind, the highlight of his selling was the handing out of little buff cards imprinted thus:

Mrs KIRKPATRICK
Corset Fitter
2a Blenheim Gardens
THANK YOU FOR YOUR PAST SUPPORT

He claimed she was a second cousin twice removed but, in actual fact, she was an agent for a clothing check company and had an underhand arrangement with Seamus whereby he took clothing checks from private patients and she got a rake-off when Seamus cashed them.

We all knew that the devious Solly was the godfather behind the little empire for he had an eagle eye for business, even if he did not actually stick his neck out and put it on the block. Behind a pewter pint pot and a battered copy of Gray's Anatomy, the master strokes of the Toomey foot empire were master-minded. Solly's Uncle Caleb had a wholesale house in Leeds which sold everything in the chemists' sundries lines, from Fuller's Earth to false teeth stain remover. Solly bought from Uncle Caleb, put on a few per cent and re-sold to Seamus, that was the idea of our Jewish friend and it was a good one as far as he was concerned for, in the long run, he was to come off the best.

Now, if it had been Solly who had started in business, it would have been no surprise because it was a part of his heritage. It was in his blood. One night he came home from the pub happy at having done a deal with one of the wide boys from Liverpool. He had bought six dozen pairs of 'Novelty Nylons', each pair saucily packed with spicy slogans printed on the covers to tickle the fancy of the ladies. Seamus got to work on these and had them sold within a fortnight. The slogan I liked best was: 'No matter how long your stocking is, the top is always nearer your bottom.'

These ventures into commerce detracted from his studies and he began to get so behind in his work that he didn't know where we were up to in the course. Such conduct could only have one end. His evenings were filled with private patients as his round grew, which was not surprising for he was under-cutting the local private chiropodist and treating people in their homes for half price. But give Seamus his due, he was good and popular with the folks who fell for his Irish blarney hook, line, and sinker, and if they hadn't flat feet when he went in the house, by the time he came out, they had, AND a pair of arch supports to prop them up. So it was not surprising that the private man got to know about it and rang Miss Hotchkiss to complain and threatened to cause a rumpus in the hierarchy of the profession if it was not stopped. What a stink was let loose then. A meeting of the Governors was called no less, and Seamus was carpeted. Would he get the bullet? Conjecture was rife and the scheming Solly made a book on it at the 'Bull and Trumpet' where the incident had attracted a lot of attention. After all, the Irish lad was the leading darts player and the team was in line to win the Brewery League Cup, so that the loss of such a star player would, indeed, be a sad loss. In fact, the lads in the pub took it so seriously that when the local private chiropodist came in for a drink, he was sent to Coventry and had to take his custom over the road to the 'Dog and Badger'.

That evening, in the digs, we were all sitting down, waiting for our meal, when in walked Seamus. He was whistling 'Danny Boy'.

"Toomey's still with you, lads, " he announced triumphantly. "I'm on me last chance so I am and, to celebrate, I'll meet you all in the pub tonight and I'll stand the booze. They might have stopped me but they can't take the profits away."

We didn't need asking twice, but it turned out that he was late arriving because he had been unrepentantly treating the local fishmonger's bunions. After all, he had half sold him on the idea of arch supports and had to finish off the deal. Seamus hadn't taken the slightest notice, so we drank our fill of his ill-gotten gains while we could, for each of us knew in his heart that he wouldn't be with us for much longer.

Just after this episode, St. Patrick's Day arrived - the 17th of March. Seamus was a fervent, patriotic Corkonian and arrived in the clinic in the morning with a huge bunch of shamrock stuck in his coat with a safety-pin. Stubbins spotted it straight away and made a bee-line for him with index finger accusingly outstretched.

"Remove that . . . that . . . clover or whatever it is, Toomey! How dare you bring bacterially receptive verdure into an aseptic clinic? Surely you know by now that such fungus is a source of infection?"

"Cobblers!" said Seamus in an aside which did not, however, miss the ears of Mr Stubbins. Our tutor coloured but said nothing. He was fuming but somehow, miraculously, keeping his temper, he did his morning chairside rounds. He was on the warpath and Toomey was on wafer-thin ice now. It couldn't last much longer. That same evening Seamus decided to throw a party. Charlie, the caretaker, and his wife agreed to put on sandwiches and the lads in the digs clubbed together for a couple of crates of beer. The party was held in the small clinic at eight o'clock when all the staff had gone home. Solly brought his concertina and we had a good old sing-song for, despite our friend's devil-may-care attitude, we knew that unless a miracle happened, he would soon be across the Irish Sea.

Seamus was a typical Yates's Wine Lodge tenor and could put over a ballad in a style guaranteed to make strong men cry and dogs bark. His rendering of 'Does your mother come from Ireland?' will for ever live in my memory as a classical example of inebriated pub singing. It was about ten o'clock when Charlie's wife asked Seamus to sing a request. He knew the song and so did Solly. He'd been over to Cork with Seamus in the holidays and they'd toured the pubs singing together and had never had to put their hands in their pockets the entire fortnight.

Full of nostalgia and Guinness, Solly played the intro- duction and Seamus burst into song.

"Oi . . .m . . .a long way from home and my thoughts ever roam to ould Ireland far over the sea. For my heart it is there where the hills are so fair and ould Ireland is calling to me. . .E. . .E

Oh! I want to go back to that tumbledown shack, to that tumbledown shack in Athlone. Just to pillow my head, on that ould trundle bed. Just to see my ould mother once more. There's a. . ."

"Toomey!"
It might have been the voice of God. It was, in fact, the voice of Stubbins.
"What is going on here, Toomey?" he demanded.
"Sure now, it's only a party for Saint Pat's night, sir," Seamus said, staggering alarmingly.
"I thought you were pleading to go back to your mother," said Stubbins. "I think that can be arranged without too much trouble."
"But, sir," said Mrs Robins, "the lads were only having

54

a sing-song. "

"In this clinic! " It was obvious that Stubbins was outraged.

"What's so special about your wotten old clinic? " Seamus demanded, buckling at the knees and unable to pronounce his r's.

It was much too late for any of us to try and repair the damage. Stubbins, normally very reasonable, was too dedicated to his clinic to have it described in such a derogatory manner without suitable retaliation. His face had lost every trace of its usual colour. He was wounded, and it showed.

"Toomey, " he said, "I will see you in the morning when, I trust, you will be sober. I see no point in continuing this discussion until you are in your right senses. " He turned and left and Mrs Robins broke down and wept. There was reason for tears. For Seamus this was the end. The following night he was on the boat ploughing its way to Ireland. There was gloom in the foot hospital, digs and the tap room at the local.

About a month later we had a letter from him. He had taken his girlfriend with him and they had set up in Ballygo-backwards or some such place as qualified chiropodists. He explained that each had done half the course, so that between them they had done the whole of it. It did not occur to Seamus that they had done the same half. I suppose that, had they both completed the course he would have claimed to be twice as good as any other chiropodist in the whole of Ireland. Certainly he would be unbeatable at one thing - the sweet, seductive talk that had people putting their money where their feet are. His dismissal had the effect intended by the Governors on the rest of us. The chance of making money on the side lost all its attraction and we were brought abruptly to our senses and made to face up to the real reason why we were all at Barn-field in the first place.

Chapter Five

All aspects of medical study are greatly concerned with the human being as a person, and not just as an anatomical and physiological specimen.

Knowing how to talk to people, how to approach and humour them, understanding their peculiarities. This is all very important to the chiropodist for he has a closer relationship with his patient during treatment than, say, a dentist has, for you can't say much when there is a pair of pliers on your bad tooth.

Of all the medical professions, chiropody is the one where the patient can sit back and have a good old natter. Very often it aids the operator if the patient does this, for it relieves any tension he might feel and so relaxes the muscles of the leg and foot which makes treatment easier.

Not that foot treatment readily vocalised every patient at Barnfield. Far from it. Some were so nervous that it was very hard to get a squeak out of them, and held their limbs so stiffly that it made treatment much more difficult. Stubbins could be most considerate and sympathetic towards nervous patients, and impressed it upon us that our manner at the very first introduction to the patient was crucial. This could make or break patient-chiropodist cooperation.

So I considered the study of human nature just as much an important aspect of the course as the other subjects. Patients are not clinical specimens. They are real, ordinary humans and it pays to be very broadminded at times. There are many types of patients, of course, but it is amazing how many try to be funny during the treatment. 'Having your feet done' seems to have an effect on the jocular vein.

I will never forget old Abe Martindale who was a regular at the foot hospital. He was a very thin, likeable old chap with a huge white hearing aid stuck in his right ear and very popular with the students. He spoke in a loud, reedy voice and always trundled out the same stories. Some of them were not exactly of the drawing-room variety but, coming from Abe, even your most sedate maiden aunt could not have taken offence. The opening gambit for most chiropodists is, "And how are your feet today?" Abe's pet answer was: "You know the railway company, London, Midland and Scottish? L.M. & S? Well, that's how I feel at present - hell of a mess," and he would roar laughing and I would have to usher him out of the back door before he had the place in an uproar.

Then there was the woman who asked me not to cut her right little toenail but to cut all the rest. On the third occasion I queried the reason, for it was like a tiger's claw by this time.

"My husband's a lazy beggar," she told me, "and there's nothing better for getting him out of bed in the morning than rubbing a good sharp toenail up and down the soles of his feet. He doesn't half hop it then!"

The district around the School of Chiropody was a noted one for the seamier side of life and it was quite a common event for males to be accosted by 'ladies' with handbags swinging on their arms. They didn't hit you with them, their technique was to ask you if you had a light for the unlit cigarette dangling from the corner of a heavily lipsticked mouth. One evening I was naive enough to stop a man and ask him for a match for the 'lady' who had requested one from me. He looked at me as if I'd just come up the river on a raft and said, "It's time you grew up, Sonny. Someone ought to tell you the facts of life. She's after more than matches, is that one."

Of course, this constant patrolling was hard on the feet and so we had quite a large number of these members of the Frail Sisterhood, as Stubby liked to call them, attending for treatment.

I often used to think how horrified Mother would have been to learn that her son was devoting some of his time to keeping the feet of the street girls of Barnfield in good shape. The jolliest one was a middle-aged practitioner who made no pretence about her calling.

"Oh my!" She sighed wearily one day after she'd climbed into the chair. "I've moved to a new flat now, dear. It means going upstairs every time with a client and I must have gone up those steps fifty times since last Saturday - oh, my poor feet!"

After every treatment she'd leave a bag of sticky un-wrapped humbugs on the trolley which I would, just as relig-iously, condemn to the dustbin.

I once heard corns and bunions described as 'the bane of

kings and paupers alike' which is, without doubt, a true saying. As Stubby delighted in trooping out year after year to all first-year students: 'The common corn is non-political, neither Labour nor Conservative, but it is most certainly liberal in its distribution!' - just another way of saying that foot troubles are no respecters of class. Though in later days I did treat a titled Liverpool race-horse owner's feet, I have never knelt before the feet of royalty. At Barnfield variety made up for any lack of notability amongst the patients, and we treated the odd clergyman, nun, and a professional tramp whilst every day a selection of people from a multitude of trades and professions came daily to the clinics. While Beecham was busy keeping the world in motion we were just as busy keeping it on its feet.

One of our most bizarre callers was a fat gentleman who always wore a black suit and tie and could have passed as a cohort of Death himself. At first I assumed that he was a local funeral director but later found out that he was one of the best known figures in Barnfield, an Evangelist and prophet of doom who patrolled the cinema queues and football crowds, calling for people to see the error of their ways. The story went that, at one time of day, he had been one of Barnfield's leading rakes but, upon the death of his mother, he had suddenly turned to the opposite direction and dedicated his life to vehemently denouncing all the vices he had formerly indulged in with such relish. As he walked down the clinic he would hand out buff-coloured tracts which proclaimed that our end was nigh. In the waiting-room his long-poled placard was a source of curiosity and amusement to the other patients. This bore the words 'THE HOUR IS UPON US - REPENT!' But despite expecting the call at any time, it was obvious that he wasn't going without his feet being comfortable, for he was one of our most regular clients.

As a complete contrast, we had Nelly who, at one time, had been a singer on the 'boards' and who, despite the passage of time, still possessed a tuneful voice. Her gimmick was entertaining in the waiting-room by singing parodies on old Music Hall songs. If the coast was clear, she would perform in the clinic while having treatment. Miss Hotchkiss had once snootily reminded her that she was in Barnfield Foot Hospital and School of Chiropody and not the back stalls of the Barnfield Tivoli. But Nelly loved to sing and entertain. It had always been her life and no bumptious person in a white coat was going to stop her. And although it is many years ago now, I can still remember the words of one song which was guaranteed to make Solly Hymans almost gyrate with laughter. So much so that one morning his patient withdrew her foot from the foot stool and adamantly refused to replace it until he ceased shaking with mirth. The words ran something like this:

Walter . . . Walter . . . lead me to the altar,
And buy a double bed . . . do!
Walter . . . Walter . . . though you're thick as Gibraltar,
I suppose you'll have to do.
Walter . . . Walter . . . I know what you're after,
To see if me bloomers are blue . . .

Well, they say that variety is the spice of life and it certainly made our time at Barnfield more interesting and enjoyable.

The tramp was a fascinating character, known simply as Joe. He refused to give details of himself, even his surname. Joe was one of the now rare breed of old type 'Gentlemen of the Road' in decrepit suit of myriad patches and holes with a sack on his back and attendant billycan and kettle hanging from it. He refused to be parted from his bundle, despite the look given him by Miss Hotchkiss, and would place it underneath the patient's high chair with all the reverence one would assume a king has for his crown. I treated Joe several times and never ceased to marvel at the cleanliness of his feet. After all, he was a tramp and did a round trip of the north of England in between his visits to the clinic. One day he told me that he scrubbed them with mud and then soaked them in a brook. He was a water cress collector and, after the treatment, would present me with a bunch, neatly wrapped in newspaper. Joe was one of the nicest and most grateful of patients and it put a damper on the clinical proceedings the day we heard the news that he had been beaten up by a gang of young thugs. I often wondered just what it was that Joe carried about in his sack.

One of the most interesting facets of the course was the insight we got into administration. Our year was split into four groups with each one undertaking a type of project. My group looked into the provision of transport for patients who were physically handicapped and unable to come to the school clinic under their own steam. We sent out letters to selected people over the age of sixty-five and some of the replies served to make it a most entertaining diversion from our normal studies and duties. One woman actually claimed to have lost her feet altogether and had 'made other arrangements'. Another wrote to say that any day would be convenient as long as it didn't clash with Haydock Park races and we, not her, mind you, would find the race dates in the daily paper. While a most appreciative old lady told us that she would welcome transport as she was finding it difficult getting breath at the local shops, a gentleman of ninety wrote to say he would deem it a great favour if he could be dropped at the 'Black Bull' on the way home. My favourite was a letter of complaint from an elderly lady criticising ambulance drivers and ended by saying 'the last time a driver came the dog bit him. If he comes again I'll ask the vet to put him to sleep'! Mind you, this letter was rivalled in appeal by one from a Mrs McTavish who informed us that she didn't consider it worthwhile coming . . . 'as I only have one leg, also one foot, and some folks have more than me'. Yet another informed us that the writer's aged mother had athlete's foot and a sprinter in her heel!

It was all part and parcel of our practical training and not only helped us in our professional approach but was a good insight into human nature, for the psychological approach to patients is just as important in chiropody as in other branches of medicine. Especially so when a patient comes to the surgery or clinic apparently without any obvious signs of discomfort but insists, often in a most vague way guaranteed almost to make diagnosis an impossibility, that she has 'bad feet'. I have found by experience that it is much more satisfactory to attempt to treat these people in some way and definitely not 'good medicine' to tell them that there is nothing wrong with them at all. Some of the old ladies simply need a sympathetic ear.

The memory of Mr O'Mulligan will never be eradicated from my mind for he stands out as a prime example of a patient who required a little kind advice and a few minutes devoting to his troubles. He arrived one morning as part of a case load of ambulance patients. A man of seventy-six, very thin and small with a beak nose that was never without an attendant 'dew drop', he shuffled up the clinic, helped by the driver, and had seated himself on my operator's stool before I could stop him. These stools usually have wheels and are rather dangerous to elderly, unsteady patients. I told him about its dangers immediately, but he took no notice.

"Oi'll tell ye about it, sor, " he began in that nasally tongue of the 'Garden of Ireland' and known as 'Whiny Wicklow'. Whether this is produced by an altitude of the district, I don't know, but it's an outstanding accent and as distinctive as 'Liverpuddlian'.

"Would you please sit in the high chair, Mr Mulligan, " I requested.

"O'Mulligan, sor - me brother's Mulligan. You see, we both have the same Christian names coming from different fathers but be the same mother, so he leaves the O off so that folks'll tell the difference, sor. Oi thought as oi'd tell you, sor, because he's a patient here as well. Now, sor, about me legs. You see, sor, I had an accident. A bus hit me two years ago and Oi've been in hospital . . . "

"I'm sorry to hear that, Mr O'Mulligan . . . but please sit on the chair and take your shoes and stockings off so I can examine your feet. "

He looked at me almost aghast.

"Fate, sor? It's me legs, sor. I want to tell you, sor, about me legs. "

He still made no effort to move off the operator's stool.

"You do need chiropody treatment, sir? " I asked him, suddenly thinking that perhaps it was one of those peculiar mix-ups where a patient ends up at the chiropodist's instead of the dentist's.

"Well, sor, it's loike this. It's the toightening and Oi'd like you to tell me if you can cure it . . . you see, sor, many years ago. . . "

He had pulled out his gnarled, old pipe and was obviously setting down to spin me a long yarn.

"On the big chair, please, Mr O'Mulligan, " and I gently removed the pipe and put it back into his coat pocker, whispering, " no smoking in the clinic, it's against the rules, you know. "

Even when he was upon the patient's high chair he was still reluctant to remove his shoes and stockings.

"It's the toightening, sor, and Oi'd be grateful to you if you could tell me what's the trouble. "

At last I managed to remove his shoes and stockings and before my very eyes on the foot rest were two beautiful feet. Old, yes, but still beautiful, free from corns, callosites, inflammation or swelling and his nails were neatly trimmed into the bargain.

"Where do you have the trouble, Mr O'Mulligan? " I queried.

"No trouble, sor, just the toightening. "

"Where does it affect you, sir? " I persisted.

"Under the fate . . . toightening, sor. "

I felt the skin and there was definitely no sign of any stretching or tightness and appeared to be perfectly normal

61

and, in fact, remarkably good for a man of his age.

"There are no corns or hard skin, Mr O'Mulligan . . . in fact, sir, your feet are a credit to you. "

"Indade they are, sor. The doctor said the very same thing. Them's as good a fate as ye'd get in the whole of the country, sor, and Oi'm tellin' you. "

"And yet you have pain in the soles. . ."

"No pain, sor. . .oh, no pain, sor . . . oh not at all, sor. "

I knew what was coming next.

". . . Just the toightening, sor. "

I could see it was going to get me nowhere continuing to discuss his feet. I would move upwards with my diagnosis.

"Tell me about your operation. Were your legs very painful afterwards? "

"Ah! Legs, sor. Indeed they were, sor, and Oi've a plate in the right one and Oi've had things done to me left one. Would that be causing the toightening, sor? "

Now we were getting somewhere but, he assured me again, he had no pain at all in his feet.

"Just the toightening. "

I was racking my brain for the next question.

"And when does this toightening - I mean tightening - strike you? "

He paused for a second before announcing, "They go toight in the noight, sor. "

Muscular damage and ligamental strain were obviously the cause of this phantom complaint so I explained to him that he experienced this sensation because of the accident but that his feet were in perfect order, and he mustn't worry about them. I also told him that I would give him a tube of skin conditioning cream which would help. When I'd returned from the pharmacy with the tube, you would have thought he was receiving a gold clock by the fuss he made.

"There's a herb for every illness, as the man said, and Oi'm turrible grateful to you, sor. . . And you say this cream's for the toightening? Sure Oi knew as you'd know the cure, says Oi to meself, this is the place to come . . . It's kindness itself y'are, sor, Oi'm sure. "

For the next five minutes his thanks came thick and heavy as he nursed the tube of cream; and in the waiting-room, as he awaited the return of the ambulance, his praises for the 'clever young doctor' could be heard by the students who were working nearby. Again, on his next visit, he was full of the joys of life, but on that lovely clear skin a nasty corn had appeared on the second metatarsal head of his right foot.

I wasn't quite sure how to open this next encounter, so I began with:

"Is the skin on your right foot tight still, Mr O'Mulligan? "

He looked at me in mild amazement.

"Oh no, sor. There's no toightening, sor, just pain. "

I removed the corn and as he left he smuggled a bottle of stout into my white coat pocket right under the snooping glances of old Stubbins.

Ever afterwards, during my stay at Barnfield, whenever a patient complained of obscure pains in his feet, they were referred to as 'the toightening'.

Most patients were content to have their feet made painless and express thanks for same. And I shall never forget Mr Alfred Whitnock, a man with a florid complexion and rather heavy of frame. He came hobbling into the hospital, obviously in pain.

"Me right foot, " he said. "Killin' me. "

Compassion dictated that I should help him remove his boot and sock. When I saw the bunion on his big toe I was shocked.

"Good heavens, sir! " I said, "You must have had a terrible time with this. "

"Oh, I have, sir. Terrible. Hurts me in bed even. "

"For goodness sake, why haven't you come sooner? "

He shook his head. "I couldn't bring myself to face it. Can't stand surgery. In plain language, cowardice. "

"You won't feel a thing, " I assured him.

"Oh, it isn't that. It's not the pain, it's the idea of it. "

He had withdrawn his bunioned foot and was hiding it behind the other.

"You just trust me, " I urged. "Put yourself in my hands and it will be over in no time. "

He eyed me doubtfully. "Are you sure? " he asked, still hiding the bunion as if it was his last penny in the wide world.

"Positive. Mind you, if you'd prefer Mr Stubbins . .? "

"No, no. I'm sure you'll do your best. "

"Oh, you can be sure of that. So if you will be so kind as to place your foot on here? " I indicated the foot rest but you would have thought I'd asked him to place his head on the block he was so hesitant.

He advanced the foot a mere inch and then stopped. In fact, it took me all of five minutes to coax that foot on the rest. Once it was there, I took firm hold of it. To gasps of alarm and squawkings of terror, I treated the bunion.

"Oh, oh dear!" Mr Whitnock panted. "I'm going to faint. I'm dying!" Beads of perspiration stood on his forehead though I was positive he did not feel pain.

"You're doing fine," I told him.

A long shuddering sigh escaped him. Then he became still. I felt his pulse. It was fast but steady. I proceeded to work on the same way - fast and steady. By the time he came out of his faint, I had finished work on his foot and it was properly bound and padded.

A glass of water and a wait of five minutes and Mr Whitnock was himself again. Or very nearly so.

"Funny things feet, doctor," he said at last. I glowed with a feeling of pride at the sudden promotion. He was looking at me in a confiding sort of way.

". . . sort of make you . . . well, put you off, don't they . . . kind of . . . well, you know . . . affect other things like . . ."

"Yes, Mr Whitnock - such as?" I quizzed, not for one second realising just what he was meaning.

"You know . . . Makes a man poorly. The wife's only young, you know."

He was gathering courage but he cast a precautionary glance around before continuing. "My foot's been putting me off. But it feels grand now, doctor - just grand! I feel a new man already. I reckon having your feet done is the finest aphrodisiac you can get. I'll take missus out to the 'Dog and Duck' tonight and I'll buy her a large port and lemon and I'll have a couple of pints of best bitter. It's even put me off drinking, doctor. Life's been proper dismal. I've often heard it said that feet can make you feel rotten all over, but I didn't know they could make me feel so bad."

"Which is the worst of the two evils, then, or, perhaps, joys missed, would be more correct?" I asked.

His only answer was a coy grin and he pressed a coin into my hand. He stood up and tenderly tested his foot on the lino. He smiled.

"No pain?" I asked.

"Not a sign. But I'll not start crowing until I've tried with me boot on."

Three minutes later he was smiling like an Israelite sighting the Promised Land. "Still no pain," he said, gingerly moving the foot around.

"There won't be," I told him.

"Doctor, I feel like a new man," he said jubilantly. He laughed with delight. "But not like a new woman. Oh, no! The woman I want is waiting for me at home right now. She's a gem. A peach! By Jove, who'd have thought life could be made so miserable by a bloody bunion."

"How long have you been married?" I asked.

"Close on twenty years, doctor."

"And you still feel like this about each other?"

"More than ever. Ours is a real love match in every way."

"Then marriage is what it's cracked up to be?"

"Depends on who's doing the cracking!" He thrust another coin into my hand and, saying thank you over and over again, turned and made for home as if the house was on fire. It wasn't, but in a very happy sense, Alfred Whitnock was.

A fortnight later, I came upon Alfred and his wife in the town's main street. The sight of Mrs Whitnock made me realise how lucky Alfred was. She was rosy cheeked, happy eyed and dimpled in both chin and cheeks, with a cracking figure thrown in for good measure.

"Doctor!" Alfred greeted me. "Meet the wife."

She disengaged her hand from his arm to shake hands with me. "I'm delighted to meet you," she said. "I owe you a great deal."

"Seeing you so happy is reward enough," I said gallantly.

"Aye," said her husband. "Life's been sweet since you did my feet. There!" he exclaimed, "You've made me a poet."

It was a title for a song, I thought. And it inspired me to dream up a quatrain Irving Berlin or Cole Porter might have turned into a winner.

'Life's been sweet since you did my feet
That spring time long ago.
Heaven knows that true love flows
Not down, but up from your toes.'

They were so grateful that they insisted I went with them to the fish and chip cafe for a meal.

Chapter Six

I have always been a firm believer in luck. If the gremlins
are working against you, then you have no chance. At least,
that is how life has always appeared to me, although I know
that luck usually favours the courageous. And in exams anyone who has worked hard deserves a bit of luck, but it is
strange how fate can twist things round the wrong way, in the
opposite direction to what we consider will happen. Like
Anatomy and the practice of Chiropody, for example. In my
own mind, I was doomed to fail the final exam in the former
and put on the performance of my lifetime in the second, which
is perhaps what I did, as you will see.

The examinations were almost upon us and I had been advised by a past pupil to obtain a leg from the local hospital.
That was, he hastened to add, if I had the stomach for the job
of dissecting it. I was so weak in anatomy that I felt I could put
up with anything if it helped in any way. So, I rang up the
hospital and asked if it might be possible to have a leg from the
mortuary. I was told that if I went along to the mortuary and
spoke to the nurse in attendance at the office I might well be in
luck.

I took Alick along with me and we were duly received at
the office by a dishy, young nurse who immediately took my
mind off a corpse's leg. Her own deliciously sculptured live
ones were far more appealing and, by the beaming smile she
gave me, I felt that there was every hope of a date if I used
some charm. 'How weak is man!' I couldn't help but muse
to myself. Half an hour before I had been having cold sweats
in the digs at the thought of the Anatomy examination and my
complete lack of comprehension of the subject. Yet here I was
all agog at the sight of a woman. She opened a large black
book and asked us to append our names.

"General Office rang to tell me you were coming for a
leg," she said sweetly and then added with an accompanying
pert smile, "always glad to help young doctors." I could well
imagine that the young doctors would be only too eager and

66

glad to help her, too. I smiled a 'thank you' and felt the age old chemistry reaction of reciprocal appreciation tingling up my spine. She fancied me, by Jove! Then, like a hat-pin plunged into a football bladder, my chances fizzled out, utterly deflated, for Alick proclaimed in a loud voice:

"We not doctors, Missy, " thereby putting his great black feet well and truly in it.

"Not doctors? " She looked at us quizzically.

I could see her mind working. We were too young for specialists and what would dentists want with a leg? What about vets? No, couldn't be . . . her mind was like a motion picture, and when Alick added, "We am chiropodists, Missy, " it was as if a great storm had erupted on the screen. She was disgusted. Her nose went up in the air.

"Feet? Corns and things? " She asked, arching her eyebrows.

If Alick had said we were a couple of rat-catchers or drain consultants, her reaction couldn't have been worse. Feet indeed! You could see disdain written all over her face. She was a doctor-hunting nurse all right and I was out of the race before it had started.

"And you want a leg? " she remarked, making no effort to hide the sarcasm in her voice.

"We are licensed to the knee, you know, " I put in defiantly, hoping that such information would raise my fallen stock from the abyss of her disapproval.

"Oh, are you? I hope you don't ever go above it, boys! I'm sorry, but medical students only is the rule here for anatomical specimens. " And, so saying, she gave us a saucy smile as she waggled her Brigitte Bardot figure down the corridor.

"Idiot! You prize pillock! Why so honest and upright all of a sudden. Just because she didn't fancy you! " I was furious with Alick.

But my black friend was not the same philandering prince I had known earlier in the course. He was terrified in case he failed, for it seemed that his father had already set him up in private practice and never, for one second, did he expect his son to let him down.

"You am no doctor, John. Now tell the truth and shame the devil, Man, " he answered seriously.

Deep down I knew he was right, of course. It was imperative that I passed also, for I was stony-broke and knew Dad couldn't keep on subbing me for ever. But anatomy was my weakest subject and the refusal of the leg was a blow. We had diagrams and books, of course. Then there was 'Fred' (the pickled foot in the formalin jar) but, somehow, I just couldn't get a clear picture of the actual coordinated workings into my head. Then, Alick came up with a good idea. He approached Stubby to see if he would lend us Cassius, the skeleton. He had been kept strictly under lock and key ever since the time Seamus Toomey had pinched him and done an Irish jig with him at the christmas party. But Stubby had a soft spot for Alick and relented upon our assurance that we would look after him like a lost son. It seemed that the skeleton had been christened by a former student who was fond of Shakespeare. Upon seeing it for the first time, he had exclaimed dramatically: "Yon Cassius hath a lean and hungry look."

Stubby liked it and the name had stuck.

Cassius was just what the doctor ordered as far as we were concerned and, together, Alick and I designed a novel way of tracing the muscles and ligaments. For the muscles we cut up strips of old white coats which had been laid up for disposal at a jumble sale. I considered that the financial state of the local league of 'Cats' Friends' was far less important than our anatomy exam and so the promised white coats never arrived at the church hall for the sale. As a balm to our consciences, we clubbed together ten bob which we put in an envelope and wrote on the back 'from a well-wisher' and pushed through the letter-box the previous evening. The ligaments were pieces of string and the veins lengths of tubing, kindly supplied by the landlord of the 'Bull and Trumpet' and formerly used for syphoning beer. By the time we had laid on layers of fat and muscular tissue in the form of old newspapers 'Yon Cassius's' legs resembled two long parcels of fish and chips. The idea was something like passing the parcel without the music. As we unravelled the coverings we said what they represented out loud together, like a couple of parrots. The mess we made every evening took a lot of clearing away, but we were both thankful that we didn't get the leg after all because, apart from the fact neither of us would have had the stomach for it, it would have been a sure way of getting the boot from the new digs which were too comfortable to jeopardise by dissecting legs in the bedrooms.

Exam fever was well and truly in the air, with everyone cramming knowledge into their skulls in a desperate last-minute effort.

Alick and I would sit for hours firing questions at each other until we were fed up with the whole thing. If we didn't know it now, we never would, for the final hour was nearly upon us when the fruits of our labours during the two years would soon be harvested in the form of exam results. I broke out in a cold sweat at the very thought of it. Consumed by a really bad attack of exam nerves, my past would float before me as I lay in bed, unable to sleep. Those hours of horse-play when I should have been studying, practical jokes, count-less pints, a proficiency at pub games above the average, dominoes and cards. Time wasted, valuable time. God given time. I'd let my parents down. I was a failure. A dismal wash-out of a son. Never could I pay them back for what they'd done, what they had given up in order to put me through the course. I'd never be a 'proper' chiropodist like my dad dreamed about. In his eyes, I'd be no better than the ex-grocer with the razor blade. I started to have terrible remorse. Really, I should have gone to the doctor, for my nerves were in a bad way and I needed some kind of tranquillizer.

But, strange as it seemed, I need not have worried over my anatomy and physiology and the other oral and written examinations. In fact, I found them surprisingly easy. My trouble was to be the Final Practical Chiropody Exam. This was the Big One, the gruelling session in the clinic under the critical eyes of the examiners, accompanied by Miss Hotchkiss. She always gave me the jitters whenever she stood behind me and I wasn't looking forward to the prospect in the Final. Even now, as a very experienced chiropodist, I must admit to a feeling of uneasiness whenever I have someone standing behind me, watching me operate.

This examination was the very last one and took a full day. Each examinee treated one patient in the morning and one in the afternoon. When the list of the examiners' names was placed on the notice-board we all got a shock. Mr Stubbins was one, then there was a visiting senior lecturer from another school, and a Reginald Cowes-Blair, Esq. This last name was the real shock to us all. If he got nasty we were for it, for it was well known that he was dead against students of Barnfield. We reckoned old Hotch had invited him to be an examiner as an act of reparation. What had happened was this: Cowes-Blair lived in a very high-class district of Cheshire called Peover Superior. A few months previously we had organised a coach tour to visit Jodrell Bank, the home of the famous telescope. But that was a blind really, for it was more of a drinking and necking outing than anything else. On the way back we called at Peover, which is the next village to Peover Superior, where we frequented the local pub and were ejected for starting a sing-song and throwing scalpels at the dart board. Spotting a notice by the cemetery which read 'Peover Church', I wrote beneath it, in chalk, 'impossible'.

Old Cowes-Blair had got to know about this unbridled frivolity and was most affronted when he found that a party of chiropody students were responsible for desecrating the church sign. His professional prestige was sorely hurt; besides, he was a most respected member of the community. He rang Miss Hotchkiss and played stink. An eminent member of the profession and highly esteemed in Peover Superior and its environs, such behaviour discredited him. He made such a fuss that old Hotch called us into her office. We denied it of course. In any case, Cowes-Blair had no definite proof that the party was from Barnfield. But we knew that he was aware of the truth.

Clive was not exactly one of his admirers, for he had made a few visits to the school in the past and had been officious with him. Miss Hotchkiss made a great fuss, of course, when these visits occurred for she loved to think that she was rubbing shoulders with the upper crust of the profession and cultivated carefully any acquaintance which would enhance her professional and social standing. So Clive, who should have been a detective and not a chiropodist, got to work to uncover the grim, murky truth about the said gentleman. What he turned up was quite a revelation, but that was all, for it didn't do us any good and we were still faced with the reality of him as an examiner at the Practical. Clive revealed that Reginald Cowes-Blair had been born Herbert Sharrocks in Rochdale and was living over the brush with an ex-circus performer from Blackpool. Solly came up with the idea that a quick phone call to the 'News of the World' would set the headlines ablaze and see him stepping down from the examination panel. Not one of us had the courage to go ahead with such an idea, however. A phoney accent and the posh name, plus a fawning bumptious manner had made him a great favourite, and he charged extortionate fees. On top of this, his training was shrouded in mystery and Clive even went so far as to say that if Cowes-Blair's greenhouse was searched, according to Mr Stubbins, who had confided in him during one of his Sunday afternoon exhibitions at his flat, dozens of red cabbage jars would be unearthed. Stubbins did not approve of the man and looked on him as a quack who had wheedled himself into the top bracket of the profession, and, if it wasn't for Miss Hotchkiss, he would soon have told him to keep his nose out of the affairs of Barnfield Foot Hospital. But, if Stubbins had to put up with him then we, as mere students, had no option but to accept the fact that he had his knife in us right at the start.

So that was the man who was to be one of the examiners, just the type to be downright awkward and expect the most from others. One slip and he would fault us and we all knew it. After what we had done in Peover Superior we would have to be on tip top form, otherwise we would be failed. The atmosphere in the digs was gloomy in the extreme and the previous night was spent stropping up our scalpels and ironing white coats, polishing shoes and gargling with mouthwash and everything else we could think of that would make us smell and look nice and perform like polished chiropodists.

The day dawned and I sailed through the morning session. My patient was a lady with very painful neuro-vascular corns beneath both her large toes which I treated painlessly and I felt reasonably sure that I had impressed the examiners. Cowes-Blair's beady eyes followed my every movement. The slightest mistake and he would have been on to me and I could almost feel the cold, bitter wind of scrutiny whistling down my neck. I felt especially pleased when the patient thanked me for my excellent treatment, and managed to slip me half-a-crown without being spotted. But how cruel fate can be! For the afternoon session turned out to be a disaster for me. The very reverse of the morning. Maybe I was over-confident after my previous success, but really it was sheer cruel luck and was to haunt me in the nocturnal hours for months afterwards. But then I'd had my piece of good luck in the anatomy exam and we have to take the rough with the smooth.

I shall never forget that patient's name if I live to be a hundred and fifty. I can see the treatment card now: 'Peter Coggins, aged 76, diabetic. Plantar Callosities B/F.' He was sitting in the treatment chair and I sat down on the stool before him and bade him a 'Good afternoon'. There was no reply. Both his feet had frightful great corns on the metatarsal regions. B/F, I hasten to add, means both feet, in the jargon of chiropody.

"We'll take Vose first, gentlemen, "I remember Stubbins saying to the other examiners. "Carry on, Mr Vose. You have a very interesting patient here, I see."

There were grunts of agreement from his colleagues who all bent foward eagerly to survey the feet in question.

As it was to turn out, Mr Stubbins's remark was the understatement of the year. For Mr Coggins was one of those annoying patients who will poke at their feet during treatment. I had just swabbed them with an antiseptic liquid prior to operating when he prodded a finger between the fourth and fifth

71

toes of his left foot.

"It's in there, mester," he informed me.

He rubbed the finger nail against the skin. Like a lot of patients, he seemed to think that chiropodists have poor eyesight.

"Yes . . . yes, sir, kindly leave it to me. Sit back now and make yourself comfortable. Relax, sir, and I'll make your feet easier for you."

I proceeded to swab the area again.

"You what?"

He hadn't heard a word I'd said.

"Relax, please." I raised my voice slightly, hoping to heaven that it didn't reveal the mounting apprehension in the pit of my stomach.

Down came the dirty nail again to repeat the rubbing process.

"It's between them two toes. Is it a Farouka? Can you get the root out?"

Once more, I gently removed his hand and swabbed the area yet again, struggling hard to keep cool.

"No, sir. It's a soft corn, but I will ease it for you." My voice was growing louder now.

"It's bloody sore, I know that."

"Quite, sir . . . please don't touch your foot, Mr Coggins."

"Eh? I'm a bit hard of hearing, you know. Shell shock in Ypres. You'll not remember that, will you?"

I was beginning to wonder if he'd been put up to it by Cowes-Blair to get his revenge for desecrating the church sign.

I stood up, took a sheet of paper from a pad and wrote on it: 'Kindly sit back and relax, sir. Please don't touch your feet.'' That was showing initiative, I thought. That would shut him up. He handed it back, unread.

"I've not got me specs. I left 'em in bookies. You'll have to shout."

I didn't bother. Every time the hand descended, I gently pushed it back. Just as I was removing my forceps, down came the hand again and, shattering my returning feeling of confidence, Mr Coggins bleated:

"Is it bleeding? I've got sugar, you know. I go septic when I bleed."

I hadn't drawn blood but I did when the points of the forceps were jerked into the tissues. Fortunately, it stopped easily. I dressed it and made a pad to separate the toes. I was sweating like mad and my stomach was churning. This was going to take all afternoon.

The fact that he was a diabetic worried me, although I knew he was having insulin injections daily, but diabetes must be treated with extreme care and any lesion to the skin carefully cleaned and dressed. For often they do not heal in the same way as people in normal health. Very often, also, there is a lack of sensation in the extremities. I made a point of handing Mr Coggins a pamphlet which warned diabetic patients of the dangers of self-treatment and placing feet on hot water bottles or toasting them by the fire. I caught sight of a flicker of curiosity on the face of Mr Cowes-Blair.

"As the patient is a diabetic, sir, I have given him a leaflet on care of the feet." I informed him. He nodded without showing any sign of emotion, but I knew that I had done the correct thing.

The huge corns loomed before me like crags in the Lake District. I still hadn't touched them. I put a new blade on the handle in readiness and set my teeth to the task.

"I've got corns on me balls," announced Mr Coggins in a loud voice. "I got 'em in the trenches, in the first war it were - right on 'em they are."

"Yes . . . yes, Mr Coggins. Sit back, please!"

A hot flush ran up my back and I felt as if my stomach was going to explode at any second.

"Can't you see 'em? They're on me. . ."

"Yes . . . yes, I know where they are, sir . . ."

"The missus has them there, too. Funny isn't it?"

Silence, I considered, was the most suitable rejoinder to that one.

"I'm a bleeder, too, mister," he added with a touch of malevolent relish.

"Yes, Mr Coggins. I'm well aware of that." I could almost hear Cowes-Blair's brain working that one out. I said a silent prayer that I had kept a tone of sarcasm out of my voice.

"Queer how they always come up on your . . ."

"Metatarsal regions," said I. "The balls of your feet take all the pressure when you walk, Mr Coggins. Now relax, sir."

"You what? I'm a bit Mutt and Jeff, you know."

Then he started to twitch and groan as I got down to the lower strata of the corns.

"Don't cut me, mester. I've got sugar."

As if in a dream, I successfully cleared the two corns on the left foot then he suddenly bent forward to scratch the area.

"Is that another? Feels like a dried pea in my shoe. "

Again, I had to swab the area before I padded it. The right foot was a replica of his left and so was his performance. No matter what I said or did he still pawed at his feet and he told me more than once that he had corns in that certain place, and so had his sisters, his cousins, his uncles and his aunts, so it must be in the family. My nerves were in shreds. Still, I removed the hand and still he twitched as I got down to the base of the corns and, overall, there prevailed a terrible, leaden silence as if it was the harbinger of doom. It was. Mine. If only I could have introduced an element of fun or old Coggins had said something witty, but the examiners wouldn't have laughed if he'd climbed down and done a Fandango in his long johns. After that it was all a nightmare. I was conscious of the movements of my hands but that was all, though I do remember getting the plaster stuck all over my fingers and Mr Coggins's trouser turn-ups, which I'm sure didn't help my case one bit.

Then it was all over and someone was thrusting a cup of hot tea into my hands.

"Here, sit down, John - old devil give you a bad time, then? Where they dig them up beats me. Here, you're shaking, have a couple of aspirins and forget it. A few pints of good tea and you'll be as good as new. "

I eased myself back into an easy chair, with my head throbbing like a steam engine. I am probably wasting ink when I tell you that I failed. But I didn't care a damn and that night I got well and truly plastered, along with Solly and Alick. They were both confident they had passed and insisted on paying for the drink which, I suppose, was some consolation. But the irony of it was that I had passed all the other subjects, including anatomy, in which I had come joint second with another student.

The day after the results were posted, I was summoned to Mr Stubbins's office.

He gave me a warm smile.

"Sit down, Vose. " The tone of his voice was at once sympathetic.

"First, let me congratulate you upon passing all the subjects but one. You see, you needn't have been so worried over anatomy. The very subject you feared, you passed with flying colours . . . Hum! but things didn't go too well in the practical, Vose. "

I nodded in silent agreement.

"If I'd picked the anatomy questions myself, I couldn't have been better pleased, I was lucky really. . ."

"But what you mean, Vose, is that if you'd had the choice of the bad feet in Great Britain you wouldn't have picked Mr Coggins's for the final practical, is that not so?"

"Exactly . . . I know a chiropodist has to adjust to all sorts of people, sir, but even an experienced one would have had trouble with that man. A stone deaf diabetic with dirty finger nails and corns on his . . ."

"Quite . . . Quite, Mr Vose . . . quite!" interrupted Mr Stubbins hastily. "I am aware that the case was difficult. You have my sympathy. You and I have not always seen eye to eye but, I must admit, I feel you are now a competent chiropodist. But if only you had kept your head at the end, laddy . . why did you have to crack?"

"I did mutter something, sir. Nerves snapped, you know. Did the other examiners hear me?"

"Hear you, Vose, hear you? The whole clinic heard you, man! 'Keep your blasted big toe still or I'll cut it off' isn't the sort of remark to come out with on your final practical, now is it? Yes, provocation was there, I know. Mr Coggins is what I'd call a 'one off' character and a more difficult patient would be impossible to find if we combed the length and breadth of England. But I'm afraid Mr Cowes-Blair was disgusted with your language and he was most adamant that this couldn't be tolerated. Rather unethical I'm afraid. However, I have arranged a re-sit for you in a fortnight's time. Two fresh examiners, both eminent and highly capable, but fair, lecturers will be in attendance. I feel sure that you will have more success at this second attempt."

He shook my hand warmly and repeated that he knew I would pass.

I did. I walked out of the school a fully-qualified, hospital-trained, brand new chiropodist and, that night, Alick, Solly and yours truly again got well and truly sozzled at the 'Bull and Trumpet'. But this time with the best excuse I could have in the whole world. For the first time in my life I felt that I had accomplished something worth while.

Chapter Seven

I really had no idea what I was going to do for a job. Two of the students has stayed on at Barnfield as full-time clinic workers, but this didn't appeal to me. I wanted to view other scenes, though I had been far from unhappy at the school. Mother and Dad wanted me to open in private practice, but both understood fully when I said that I felt I needed more experience first. Chiropody within the Health Service was spreading slowly but there were not many jobs available at that time. I applied for two. One was taken and the other, at Blackborough, was filled temporarily but the letter gave me hope that a job would become vacant later on, when I would be given the chance of an interview.

Just as I was beginning to get anxious and deciding that a private practice it would have to be, I received a telephone call from Taffy Evans. I had been friendly with him at Barnfield although he had been on an earlier course and had qualified six months before me. He told me that he was in practice in north Wales and already known as Evans the feet. Had I got a spot? I had to report a blank and admit that the prospects were not too rosy. "Then why not ring up a Mr Cowthorpe in the Rossendale Valley, boyo? He's going into politics or something, thinks he has a chance to be an M.P. so he wants an assistant to stand in while he's busy."

I wrote down the telephone number, eagerly, and as soon as our conversation was over I was dialling the number in Rossendale.

The voice which answered was a deep Lancashire one and warmed at once to my request for an interview. I could see him the very next day as he needed someone very quickly. I tried to give him some details of my training but he didn't seem interested and said all that could wait until we met, in the 'Swan with Two Necks' public house in Todmorden at one o'clock the next day. The publican would point him out to me.

After our phone call, I looked at the map. While Todmorden was not that far away from his home which was near

Rawtenstall, It was still twelve miles away and I couldn't help but wonder why I couldn't have met him at his surgery or in Rawtenstall. Still, that didn't really matter. The fact was that it looked as though I'd landed a job.

So, the next morning saw me taking a train to Manchester, where I changed for Todmorden. The 'Swan with Two Necks' turned out to be a cosy little pub and full of lunch-time drinkers. There was no need for me to speak to the publican for a very large, red-faced man approached me as soon as I entered the bar.

"You Mr Vose, lad? " he asked.

I nodded.

"Dick Cowthorpe. "

He stuck a large limp hand into mine which was akin to sticking your hand into a plateful of tripe. His ginger moustache looked all the more unusual because he hadn't a hair on his head. All of six feet in height and sixteen stones in weight, he sported a red shirt, a loud, plaid sports-coat and a blue-and-white spotted dicky bow. Green corduroy trousers and brown brogues completed the discordant ensemble. The whole effect was gawdy and ostentatious. All he was short of was a board proclaiming that he was 'Honest Dick, turf accountant', for he certainly gave the impression that he belonged to the racing fraternity rather than the chiropody profession. Or maybe he specialised in horses' feet! Or was this Taffy Evans's idea of a joke?

"So you're lad who rang me? Just caught me, too. I were on't way to council meeting. 'Appen it's mayor, I thought, but it were right welcome when I heard you say as you were wanting the job. I've got a big round on't feet job, you know. "

He took my by the arm and escorted me into a small, snug room which was completely empty and smelled of polished upholstery and stale beer.

"Ideal place for a chin-wag, lad. Sit you down. What's it going to be? Bitter, mild or a drop of the hard stuff? "

"Thank you, Mr Cowthorpe, I'll have a half of bitter, " I replied politely, though I was rather put off by the man and his jarring voice. Up to then I had imagined all chiropodists were similar to Mr Stubbins. There was something about him which I couldn't quite put my finger on.

"Gill of Local, Harold! Same again for me! " he bellowed through a tiny hatch which connected with the bar. When they were put on the counter of the hatch Richard Cowthorpe brought them over to the table, which was situated close to the dart board.

"Do you throw arrows?" he enquired. "Good team here if you do, but you'd be better joining the 'Dog and Tinker' up Crook o'Nook if you like throwing. It's much nearer too."

"No, Mr Cowthorpe," I replied, "I don't play darts very much," at the same time being rather surprised that his first question about me should be on the subject of darts, though I couldn't help but wonder if he'd heard about the proficiency of the darts team at the 'Bull and Trumpet'.

He took a long pull at his pewter pot, then said, "As I told you on phone, I'm taking up politics more seriously now. I have a big practice - three days in surgery and two days and one evening outside. . ."

"Domiciliary?" I broke in.

"You what? Oh, aye . . . that's right and I'll expect you do same. I'll still do odd session, bear in mind, but you'll have run of place. I'll put another chair in then I can always do a session when I'm not on council business. It's twelve quid a week. Wife's a good, homely lass and she's forever brewing up and dishing out plate pies and parkin. Mrs Sutcliffe, up lane from surgery, puts folks up and she's free at present. Good sort is Hilda, good cook, and looks after her lodgers - especially good-looking ones, lad. Mind you, you're a bit scraggy looking. Fattening up with good Lancashire grub's what you need." He cackled coarsely and gave me a dig in the stomach with his elbow. "Elligible widow, is Hilda. Well, lad, will't take it?" he concluded.

"I haven't got a car, Mr Cowthorpe. . ." I began.

". . .Don't worry on that score, lad. I'll fix transport . . well?"

I was racking my brain for questions. All the ones I had rehearsed on the train journey had deserted me. The manner of the man had completely taken me by surprise. I just didn't know what to say. I started to stammer, "But . . . well . . . will it be convenient to visit your surgery . . . I'd like to see it."

"No, lad," was the blunt answer. "Too busy - council, you know. Time-consuming local government. They're always after you. Feet were hectic enough, but it's all go in this game - don't fret over that, lad. Surgery's grand, conditions too, and folks are champion round these parts. Now I can't say fairer than that, lad, can I? Do their feet good and you'll be top of the Hit Parade with the old women," he wound up.

There seemed to be no answer to that. I began to talk about Barnfield, but he was exchanging some remarks about racing pigeons with the publican so I didn't pursue it. When he turned round, he got to his feet.

"Well, lad, I'm off. Settled, is it? Don't need start while Monday. You'll not regret it, lad."

It was Friday then and he added, "Come up on Sunday night. You've got the address? Good. Well, what about it, lad?"

"I'll take it, Mr Cowthorpe," I replied. Indeed, at that moment there seemed nothing else that I could say.

He squeezed the tripe-like hand once more into mine and said I'd not regret it and, with that, he sang out a farewell to all and sundry and as he left said in a loud voice to a man by the door, "I'll fix it with Town Clerk, Albert, don't you fret, lad," and disappeared through the swing doors.

It must have been one of the quickest interviews on record. Cosy though the pub was, I didn't stay any longer but made my way back to the station, rather flabbergasted by it all. On the way home I thought about this strange man who seemed more like a shady bookmaker than a chiropodist. I felt sure Mr Stubbins wouldn't have approved. Besides, what school had Mr Cowthorpe trained at? I suddenly realised that I knew absolutely nothing about him. I hadn't even got one of his cards. It was my own fault. I should have asked more questions and yet I had the unmistakable impression that he didn't want me to do so. The hustle and bustle suddenly seemed a set plan. I was angry with myself but then again, I wasn't used to interviews. By the same token, he hadn't asked me any pertinent questions either. I'd told him on the phone I had trained at Barnfield and that was all he knew about me, but maybe that was sufficient? The fact was, I had landed a job and Dad and Mother were delighted.

The next day was spent in packing and having my coats ironed and in cleaning my visiting case which my mother had bought for me as a christmas present. I was a professional man now and I intended to act like one. Twelve pounds was quite good then, and it wasn't that far from home and I'd be my own boss more or less, and, in any case, maybe I'd misjudged Mr Cowthorpe. I even began to feel guilty about my first impression of the man, and by the time I'd landed in Rawtenstall via a train and three buses I had persuaded myself that he was a decent enough type and I was going to like him and enjoy working in a flourishing and respected practice. Much to my surprise, I found that Barn Lane was yet another bus ride out of the town along lanes which led into the Fells. The hills looked grey and uninviting in the coming dusk of the misty autumn evening. Bleak dourness, typical of the first

79

impression one has of these regions of the industrially surrounded higher reaches of Lancashire and Yorkshire. But first impressions are not always correct and I was to find that they were not so regarding this district for, in the months which followed, I was to grow very fond of the rough moors with their stony tracks and endless dry walls of piled black stones which criss-cross the seemingly endless fell land.

But my ponderings on the view which stretched above and away from me to misty crags were suddenly jarred by the conductor's voice. I was back to reality.

"Barn Lane. Where're you going?"

It was obvious from my two suitcases that I was a stranger. Besides, these bus conductors knew all the local residents personally. It was that sort of district.

"Number 6, Sheepfold Cottage," I said.

"Dick's place? Foot chap? It's up lane and on right," he informed me.

I thanked him and jumped down at the foot of the lane, which rose almost sheer from the main road. It was hard enough to climb the hill with a pair of good feet which made the setting for a chiropody practice seem all the more unlikely. The road was lined by hawthorn bushes, past their bloom of sweet-smelling blossom. Water ran down the ditches under the hedges and the squawking of fowls pierced the evening air. I passed several smallholdings and then I saw a notice nailed to a post long-since the abode of woodworm. It stated simply:

R. Cowthorpe, Chiropodist

A wooden arrow pointed in the direction of a white cottage just visible through brambles and apple trees and set well back from the lane. I had to walk another fifty yards before I came to the garden gate and I couldn't help but think that if the patients' feet were not sore beforehand they would be by the time the surgery was reached. I never did find out why the sign was so far away from the gate, but I can only surmise this was a ploy to prevent patients from turning back before the long pull up the hill. Refreshed with hope at seeing the notice, they would hobble on thinking they were almost there. I opened the gate and the rusty squeak set up such a hullabaloo of farmyard noises that I was startled out of my wits. Ducks, hens, turkeys and all manner of fowls with their offspring and feathered relations, including a most evil-looking goose which frightened me more than any bulldog, surged over and under the flimsy wire-netting which was supposed to keep them off the path. I'd disturbed the peaceful Sunday evening siesta of the feathered world. A huge alsatian loped menacingly through the scrimmage like a long-fanged wing forward out to wallop the cheeky little scrum half. I had visions of being torn to bits as this ugly beast fought over me with the noisy poultry. From the look of him, he could have polished the lot off and then had me for supper, although the goose looked as if it could have given the Hound of the Baskervilles a run for its money, never mind the alsatian.

I was relieved to hear a human voice.

"You got here, lad, I see. I said to Richard as you wouldn't get here while evening. I put tea off until you came. Get away, Sally lass! Come for your tea, Nelly . . . chuck chuck . . . chick . . . chick . . . nice girl! Chuck . . . chuck . . ."

A large, bare-armed woman was standing in the middle of the chicken run, her right hand scattering feed from a bucket. There was a mass retreat at that, which left only Nelly, the goose, and Sally, the alsatian, glowering at each other over the human intruder upon their territory.

"Come on, Mr Vose. I'm Richard's wife. Ee, but you do put me in mind of our Fred what's gone to London to be a policeman. Brew's mashed. It'll put you on while knife and fork tea. Sure you could do with a mugful after journey, lad."

I followed her inside the cottage but before I put my feet over the threshold, I stopped to glance at a mildewed brass plate which was hanging by loose screws to the wall of the cottage. It proclaimed:

R. Cowthorpe (H.M.) A.S.A.F.C.
Chiropodist and Manipulation Consultant

"Well known in valley is Richard," said Mrs Cowthorpe in answer to my glance. "It don't seem five minutes since he put it up. You don't know how glad I am he's got an assistant. Fond of politics is my Richard. 'Appen he'll rest easy now as he's got someone to take over t'practice, and from one of best training schools and all. . ."

This was my chance.

"Did Mr Cowthorpe train at Barnfield?" I asked.

There was no guile in Mrs Cowthorpe and she was telling the truth when she answered:

"Couldn't tell you, lad. He were at it when I met him. It were a corn on me little toe what got us acquainted. We did our courting in t'evenings up Top o' th' Spring and Rakefoot. Lovely it is up there when weather's clement. Mind you, that were when Richard was doing feet from his parents' house. He set up here when we bought the cottage.

As she was telling me this, she ushered me into the kitchen, shepherding me on to an ancient deep-cushioned couch. It was a typical farmhouse kitchen, warm and comfortable in an untidy, homely fashion, but spotlessly clean. She poured me a pint mug of tea from a great mug pot.

"Drink that, lad. It'll cheer you up until I've got tea ready. There's some nice ham off the bone and lettuce and piccalilli with us own onions and cucumber. We're proper country folks up here."

While I drank the tea she gabbled away about the district and the places I'd be visiting and the old folk who lived in the smallholdings and isolated cottages on the fells, and there was such a simple friendliness about her that I took to her instantly. She uncorked a tall lemonade bottle and began topping up a wine glass which she'd wiped clean with the tail of her pinafore.

"Take a glass of rhubarb wine to your tea, Mr Vose? Home grown and home made it is. Mind you, there's nothing worse than rhubarb for rheumatics but then you'll know that already, being a chiropodist." I didn't enlighten her that I was totally ignorant of that theory, it was one Mr Stubbins had not told us about.

After we'd chatted for about ten minutes, she said, "You'd like to see the surgery, I'm sure. You go in while I get the tea. Richard's a bit funny when it comes to t'surgery, he doesn't like me interfering; says I'll only tidy everything up then he'll not know where things are. So I leave it to him, then I don't get into trouble." She laughed in an embarrassed sort of way and began busying herself clearing the kitchen table in readiness for tea.

Although she had forewarned me in her own way, I wasn't expecting the sight which greeted me when I entered 'the surgery'. My dreams of a modern, pleasant surgery were immediately shattered, but the first thing to strike me was the carpet. We had been lectured on surgery upkeep and hygiene and the idea of a carpet was taboo. Tiles or lino were far more acceptable. The walls were grubby and covered in wallpaper which, I imagined, had started out as yellow but which was now covered by a sort of khaki mildew. The patients' chair was an ancient armchair, elevated on a wooden platform, horse hair protruded from the upholstery in places and it looked the most uncomfortable seat possible to imagine. The operator's chair was an old bath stool which had been covered by a layer of chiropody felt. This was chiropody as practised in the middle ages, but there was worse to come.

Two notices were pinned to the wall with drawing pins. The first one listed fees.

One foot	5/-
Two feet	7/6d
Three feet	1 yard
Massage & Heat	5/-
Full Massage	10/-

(chaperone provided for ladies)

But it was the other that staggered me, so much so that I spilled my tea onto the carpet. It read:

Duck eggs	6/- a doz.
Hen eggs	4/6d a doz.
Cracked Ducks	4/- a doz.
Cracked Hens	3/- a doz.
Goose Grease	1/6d Bottle.

(Ideal for rheumatics, arthritis, piles, stiff necks etc.)

Fowls to Order

Xmas orders booked from October.

Still struck by a spasm of bewildered amazement, my eyes took in the full sordid dinginess of the room. My God, I had dropped on one of the very charlatans old Stubby had preached about! Of all the fowls in Dick Cowthorpe's yard, he was the biggest quack of the lot and more likely to be found listed in the Poultry Keepers' Year Book than in any list of qualified chiropodists. I had a terrific urge to take flight. My professional pride, brand new though it was, rebelled at the sight. But curiosity got the upper hand and I was compelled to delve further.

Under the price lists was an archaic massage couch which had a multi-coloured table-cloth hanging down to cover the space beneath. Warily, I lifted one corner. The space was packed with egg cartons. Small ones for hen eggs and large ones for the end product of the duck. Where he kept the goose grease I couldn't see; probably in the medicament cupboard, if this ramshackle of a surgery possessed such a luxury. I located it, standing upon a table which was heavily stained with cigarette burns and iodine. When I leaned on it, there was a groan and it lurched dramatically on the nearest left-hand leg, which was half an inch shorter than the others. It was a bathroom cabinet which at one time had been screwed to the wall, for the holes were still visible in the plaster. Inside, I found

a large bottle of iodine, some grubby cotton wool, a collection
of styptic pencils and a tin of sticking plasters. Immediately,
Stubbins's description of Septic Syd on Wigan Market came to
my mind. Had he settled in Rossendale or was this man his
pupil? The place was about as aseptic as a rag and bone man's
yard and didn't even boast a wash-basin. There was no nail
drill, needless to say, and no electric plug to run one from in
any case. If I'd had a car, I would certainly have jumped into
it and headed straight home, but I hadn't, and there was no way
of getting home at that time of night.

Looking round the room in despair, a faded notice pinned
to the wall took my attention. The name of a well-known
national newspaper was rubber-stamped on the top and underneath, in handwriting, were the words: 'Copy of Advert'. It
read:

Cowthorpe's celebrated method of Bunion straightening
during sleep. Send £1 for FULL AMAZING COURSE!

This intrigued me, to say the least, especially knowing
full well that all forms of advertsiing were frowned upon by
the Society who governed Barnfield and the other training
schools. Weeks later I was to find a dog-eared pamphlet which
described this 'revolutionary' idea. Mr Cowthorpe claimed
that a bunion (the younger the better, he pointed out, no doubt
as a loophole) could be forced back to its original state by
placing it in the crook made by bending the other leg at the
knee. The idea, seemingly, being that as the leg straightened
during sleep the bunion would be forced back beyond the pain
barrier. For two bunions he went into a complicated explan-
ation, complete with diagrams for alternating the treatment.
I never did find out if, in fact, it worked, but it did make me
realise more than ever that I was working for a man who was
unique amongst the practitioners of chiropody if nothing else.
Just then, in walked Mrs Cowthorpe to announce that tea was
ready.

"Had a good look round, then?" she asked, smiling. "If
you're wondering where to put your instruments, don't worry.
Dick works from his visiting bag, but I've painted an old table
for you - one our Fred used to do jig-saws on when he were a
kid. Loved jig-saws did Fred. He had a lovely one of Cornish
Riviera. I've painted the table white - more clinical, I thought.
It's a bit tacky yet and it's hardening in't shed, but it'll be
ready for Tuesday when your first surgery patients come.
Miss Rowbottom's first and she's a bit fussy, her being a
spinster. So I want it dry, nice and glossy. Oh, and while on't

subject of Fanny Rowbottom, she's a bit funny about taking off her stockings, so Dick always stops in't kitchen while she undoes her suspenders. Married women never bother."

After a nice tea I went back to Barn Lane to meet my landlady. Dick Cowthorpe was busy on council business so there was no point in waiting for him. That rather daunting prospect would have to wait until the morning!

Chapter Eight

Hilda Sutcliffe lived up to the glowing recommendation
Dick Cowthorpe had given her. A nice, homely woman she
made me feel at ease immediately. I had a comfortable bed in
a warm, well-decorated bedroom commanding a wonderful
view of the fells and in every possible way it was the direct
opposite to Mrs Crabshaw's digs at Barnfield.

The next morning, after a slap-up Lancashire breakfast
of porridge, two eggs, sausage, black puddings and fried
bread, topped with a pint mug of tea, I set off up the lane to
commence my duties. After a good night's sleep I felt in
better form and my spirits had risen, so it was a feeling akin
to missionary fervour that flooded my being as I walked up to
the house with the pungent tang of good cow dung heavy on the
morning air. I just managed to reach the sanctuary of the open
front door before Nelly and Sally tore the seat out of my
trousers.

Once inside I started to think. I, John D. Vose, would
bring this practice up to the highest professional level. Good
training, just like good breeding, will out and I would bring to
bear all the techniques and modern methods used in Barnfield
Foot Hospital in this practice in the Rossendale Valley.

I was aware that there were similarly trained chiropodists
as myself in the district, and I was determined that Richard
Cowthorpe's practice would be held in the same high esteem.
Not many did domiciliary visiting but, according to his wife,
he had started it up so that he could combine it with his egg
deliveries. I had made my mind up on one thing and was
adamant not to budge an inch even if he insisted: not under any
circumstances would I deliver eggs and poultry.

I found Dick Cowthorpe, resplendent in red shirt and
yellow braces, sitting at the kitchen table, eating his breakfast. He couldn't speak for a while as his mouth was full of
fried bread. His wife thrust a pint mug of tea into my hands
and pummelled the cushions of the armchair by the fire to
make them more comfortable for me to sit on.

"Like digs, lad?" asked my employer at last, when he'd wiped his mouth on a blue serviette.

"Marvellous, Mr Cowthorpe," I said. "I'm sure I'll be very happy there."

"Damned sure you will. Nice lass, Hilda. Widder, you know. So watch it, lad! 'Appen she'll fancy you . . ."and he gave a coarse and silly laugh.

"Don't be so vulgar, Dick," broke in his wife. "Hilda's old enough to be Mr Vose's mother and well you know it." She was obviously cross at her husband's remark and thought I was offended. But Dick just grinned and stuffed a piece of marmalade toast into his mouth.

"Many a good tune on an old fiddle, eh lad!" he said. "Well, let's get started and sort work out. Here's list of today's visits. And this book contains all t'house calls. T'other one in surgery is for patients what come here. That's tomorrow. Reet . . . let's see, Clara Sidwell's first - second farmhouse on right when you've climbed broo that leads up to't fell at foot of this lane. Rooted corns and double bunions." He then proceeded to give me a run down of the patients and how to reach them, plus a map of the area.

"Now, there's some folk in book who I'm keeping, sort of folk that don't like change. It's often same when they've had one fellow for years. I've put a cross by t'side of 'em so don't call there. When you've done feet, put 'em down for another appointment every five weeks."

When I pointed out that it might be difficult parking the car in some of the less accessible spots on top of the fells, he looked at me strangely.

"What car?" he asked.

By the look on his face you might have thought I had requested a helicopter. I reminded him that he had mentioned he would provide transport at our meeting in Todmorden.

"So I will, lad - so I will," he said. "Freda, lass! Show Mr Vose the Rudge. Good make, Rudge - I've pumped up tyres and there's a platform on back for your case. I did it for years on bike while I got car so it'll do you no harm, big strapping lad like you."

Rather staggered at the revelation I didn't make any comment. I collected my visiting case out of the surgery. I had my own instruments but he was providing the dressings and medicaments, which were kept in an old shoe box. They comprised a roll of plaster, a bottle of iodine, a pile of visiting cards and a pair of bicycle clips. On further inspection, I found a tin of 'Foggett's Magic Corn Cure and ingrowing toe

87

nail remover - by appointment'. Who to, I wondered, the Spanish Inquisition? The formula on the tin was lethal enough to take the paint off the park railings. I felt like a traitor to Mr Stubbins and had the unmistakable guilty feeling that he was peering over my shoulder.

I then followed Mrs Cowthorpe into the garden and saw the bicycle leaning against the hen shed. I also caught sight of the 'Instrument' table 'hardening' next to the lawn mower. The bike was a tall upright and hadn't been cleaned or overhauled for many a year, though amazingly enough it worked. But the seat was an abominable creation with a high ridge right in the centre, known to older members of the cycle trade as 'pile pushers'.

Back in the cottage, Dick gave me another list, saying, "Mrs Cowthorpe'll put the boxes in the case on the back of the bike. There'll be enough room to strap your instrument case on top. "

"Boxes, Mr Cowthorpe? " I queried.

"Aye, egg cartons, " he replied. "Go easy over't bumps otherwise they'll complain if they're broken - here's a list. Don't forget it's brown ones for Mrs Ramsbottom and the duck eggs are for the Parish priest of St. Gregory's. "

I felt my adrenalin rising. Now was my chance.

"Oh no, Mr Cowthorpe, I'm sorry, but I don't deliver eggs. "

"You what, lad? " he snapped. "I've always done it and what's more, lad, I'll have to deduct any breakages out of your wages, especially duck eggs. Tanner an egg - it's only fair. "

"I'm sorry, Mr Cowthorpe, " I insisted, "but you will have to find another chiropodist, one who will deliver eggs, for I won't do it. I want to make that plain right at the start. I'm a chiropodist, not a grocery lad. Feet not foul! "

Dick looked at his wife, her face reddened. I stood with the bicycle clips dangling in my hands, steadfastly determined not to deliver eggs. Why, if I once started that, I could see myself delivering poultry at christmas, not to mention rhubarb of which there was a prolific crop in the plot.

"I'll do it, Dick, " said his wife suddenly, busying herself clearing the table.

"No, lass. How't hell can you go scrawping up fells with them veins of yours? It's part of job - always has been part and parcel of t'practice. No, let's get cards on table, lad. "

I was all for that.

"When I met you at Todmorden, you didn't mention anything about eggs. In fact, you didn't mention the bicycle. Also,

I was led to believe transport meant a car. I mean, it usually does. "

"Car!" he barked. "Who does he think I am - Billy Butlin? Car . . . foot game don't run to two cars. I'd look well doing me rounds of town on a bike while you use the car. "

"'Appen you forgot to mention eggs, Dick, " put in his wife.

Dick snorted and blew his nose noisily on a red handkerchief. After a few wipes, he said, "I'll give you ten bob a week more if you'll do deliveries. Mind you, it's still a tanner off for every one broken and I'd be losing brass on duck eggs at that. "

"No, sir, "I said, shaking my head. "In fact, Mr Cowthorpe, I feel it would be best if I left now seeing that there has been a misunderstanding, " and I picked up my case, ready to leave.

"Nay, wait lad, " he said, hastily. "I admire your pluck for standing up to me . . . "

"There's no pluck in it, Mr Cowthorpe, " I interrupted, "I trained as a chiropodist and I won't do any other duties, it's as simple as that. "

He looked hard at me for a few seconds then forced a laugh to cover up his obvious annoyance.

"He'd be a good 'un in council chamber, would Mr Vose, Freda - eh, lass! 'Appen I'll take him with me on't knocker when I'm elected. . . "

He blew another great trumpeting raspberry into his red handkerchief and I could see beads of sweat running down from his eyes. He was annoyed about having to give way but was trying his hardest not to show it. I had won the first round and so, without any further argument, I went out into the back to collect the Rudge.

After two hundred yards I was forced to dismount from the cycle to stick a strip of chiropody felt along the saddle. Mind you, even when I'd doctored it up I still got a nasty shock whenever I ran over a pothole and on the domiciliary round there were farm tracks, footpaths over the fells, and muddy fields to be negotiated, all serving to make cycling hard work.

My first patient, Mrs Sidwell, called me a 'gradely' chiropodist and told me that my hands were much warmer than Mr Cowthorpe's. Warm hands are a blessing to the chiropodist because there is nothing more guaranteed to discourage patients than having their feet fondled by two blocks of ice. One of my present patients - a retired school mistress - never omits to give me my orders before she is treated, saying, "Now don't touch my feet before you warm your hands under the hot tap, young man. " She told me that her late husband had such cold feet that she insisted that he washed them in hot water before he got into bed.

Something which I am sure is unique in the profession was the arrangement that the patient provided the padding and cotton wool. That way, Dick Cowthorpe was on a hundred per cent profit. I had a wonderful first day. Everyone greeted me in a very friendly fashion and all seemed entirely happy with the treatments. Cups of tea, plate pies, chip butties were all offered to me. I could have got as fat as a pig if I'd continued in the way I began on that first day but I knew these folk were trying their best to be hospitable and I didn't want to hurt their feelings. Mind you, the bike riding up and down those roads and fell tracks tired me out and on the first night I fell asleep in Mrs Sutcliffe's armchair after I'd had my tea.

Even on that very first day a Mrs Aspinall told me that as far as chiropody went she didn't rate Dick Cowthorpe very highly, though it appeared that the Cowthorpe eggs were celebrated throughout the district so that people thought twice about dispensing with Dick's services. It was little wonder, then, that he was concerned about the egg round.

It was obvious from the state of the feet I treated that he only half did the job, and as he was in and out inside fifteen minutes - including the egg transactions - the chance of his patients' feet being made comfortable was a slight one.

As the weeks rolled by, any reticence on the part of his patients to comment upon the treatments began to melt. Also, I began to hear 'things' about Dick Cowthorpe. My chief confidant was a fussy old dear who hugged and kissed me after the treatment. She had a regular fortnightly visit, because her feet were so bad, and would drop hints about Dick's 'goings on' in the valley which I assumed meant with women. One day when I called she was particularly vocal on the subject.

I found that she had a sprained ankle so I applied a crepe bandage and told her to rest. She made such a fuss about my 'great skill' and then began to let rip about Dick's love affairs. It seemed they were the talk of the district. She named several of the women and I found that they were the very ones he'd told me not to call on. The ones with the crosses against their names on the list! All this was very embarrassing to me for he was my employer, even if he was a charlatan, so I would remain silent. What he did was no affair of mine so I just continued to take it all in and say nothing, for I was determined not to get involved in local gossip.

I was concerned simply with treating each patient as well as I could. Mind you, with the lack of dressings and medicaments this was made very difficult. I even bought a few items myself which I knew was silly and letting down my image of the first day when I'd refused to deliver eggs. But the truth was that I didn't really want to be involved with Dick and certainly he didn't want to be involved with me as far as chiropody went, for he seldom appeared in the surgery (I call it that for want of a more suitable word and for convenience sake). I was a stop-gap while he carried on with his politics, which had obviously consumed him with ambition, and as long as I kept his practice ticking over he was happy. It would have been nice for me if I could have looked on the job in the same way but jobs were hard to get. In fact, Dick should have been very happy for soon new patients were ringing up for appointments and one woman actually came all the way from Bacup in a Rolls Royce. It was wonderful experience for me, although I didn't fully realise its value at the time, for only in retrospect does the full value of such experience become apparent. Most appealing was the freedom, so different from the Barnfield clinics where we were always under supervision even when advanced second-year students. I was my own boss to a very great extent and many of the cases were most interesting. Although I was rather nervous at first, I soon began to stamp my own personality upon the treatments. I gave patients advice which was in direct contrast to that they'd had from Dick Cowthorpe. "Always dip your razor blade in boiling water before you cut your corns, " was one of his favourite slogans. I told these patients that under no circumstances should they use a razor blade. The diabetics had very little knowledge of foot care and, in fact, several had no idea that their complaint made them more vulnerable to infection. I had an awful job to persuade two of the diabetics that soaking their feet in concentrated caustic soda represented a great risk; several of them asked Dick for a second opinion but he simply told them that I was doing the treatments. In fact, chiropody seemed to have lost all interest for him as the election for the candidature came nearer.

Although Mr Stubbins had told us about old wives' tales for so-called foot cures, I came across several which he had not mentioned. Some were harmless enough though others were positively dangerous, not to mention revolting. Fasting spittle for corns - dip your index finger into your mouth as soon as you awake, then dab it on the painful corn. Soaking in 'lant' for sore inflamed feet. 'Lant' is a Lancashire word for urine. One old dear I called upon quite recently told me that she applied it to her leg ulcer when it was irritable during the night.

The strangest 'cure' of all was used by a widow of an undertaker's embalmer. She rubbed embalming fluid on the soles of her feet until they became inflamed and, subsequently, infected. She ended up in hospital and was lucky not to become a customer of her late husband's profession earlier than she did.

The local hairdresser showed me a bottle which bore a faded label.

"I'm keeping this as a collector's piece," she said, as I read the label which proclaimed that it was 'Cowthorpe's root killer for Corns and Warts'. She went on to tell me that she had kept the bottle as a souvenir of a good spanking her mother had given her when she was a girl of fourteen.

Twenty-five years before, Dick was just starting up his practice then and had a very profitable side-line making the concoction which had previously been in the bottle. When Dick extracted a corn he would dip a matchstick into the fluid then let a drop fall into the cavity 'to kill the roots'. He sold a bottle to her mother and, the curiosity of youth being too strong for the girl to resist, she had a smell at the contents and accidentally spilled it on the window-sill. Next day the paint rose up in blisters and, gradually, bare blotches were left all over the newly painted woodwork.

"If it would do that to paint, just think what it would have done to Mother's feet, so perhaps I did her a favour. Anyhow there were a lot of rumours at the time about someone suing him over blood poisoning and that was the end of the Corn Cure Empire. Mind you, his eggs are good; I'll say that for Dick."

And so I was gradually building up a picture of the type of man my employer was. But if he thought he was fooling the people with his new-found enthusiasm for local politics, he was very much mistaken. They'd long ago tumbled his good works and errand running as vote catching. As a rule he just said he'd 'see about it' and did nothing. But since he'd given up the chiropody, never had so many jobs been done by the council. He was the people's personal slave and the object behind it was the proposed general election. He was hoping to be chosen as a candidate to fight for a seat at Westminster and so spent his time buttering up the locals as hard as he could.

We did meet occasionally at the cottage but he didn't mention chiropody if he could help it. I knew for absolute fact that several patients had praised me to him and, although I didn't know it then, this was annoying him considerably and building up in his mind for the first of several rows we were destined to have.

Of all things, Molly Thistlethwaite's toe nail was the cause of the first one. She lived in a little white-washed cottage up on Top o' th' Spring. She wasn't on my list though I was aware that Dick used to call on her at one time. On the way past one morning, I met a district nurse coming out of the front gate. I was pushing the bike up the 'broo', completely shattered and looking forward to the free wheel down to Tom Rawlinson's farmhouse where I was sure of a mug of tea and a piece of home-made fruit cake. But the look the nurse gave me put thoughts of even that delicacy out of my head. She was a lovely little thing and though it wasn't spring - that time of year when the chiropodist's fancy, just like the young man's, turns to thoughts of love - there was springtime in my heart when our eyes met.

"Good morning, Sister, " I greeted her and there was a puff in my voice.

"Cycling's hard work, " she said in an attractive Irish lilt. "I suppose you are the insurance man Molly's been expecting. "

"No, I'm the chiropodist, " I enlightened her.

"Well, and isn't that the strangest thing? I'm only after telling her she must get something done about her nail. It would frighten the divil himself so it would - would you ever come in and look at it? She's threatening to have a go at it with a hack-saw! I think you're the answer to the old girl's prayers. "

I was only too eager to please and flattered at the same time that I had been asked to give my professional opinion by a nursing sister and, what was more, I fancied the look of the girl.

I have described the horrific specimens in the Stubbins's collection but even he did not possess a specimen of onxchogryphosis of such extraordinary character as the one which protruded from the big toe of Molly Thistlethwaite's left foot. It was like something thought up by Edgar Allan Poe in his most horrific creative mood. From base to tip, not counting its cavity-ridden curves and vagaries, it measured two inches and had the colour of a pickled walnut. She was very embarrased and didn't want to show it to me but when the nurse assured her that I was a chiropodist, she reluctantly agreed, but she was convinced it was something terrible and beyond the scope of ordinary mortals.

"It's no use, Mister, you can't do anything. I've had Mr Cowthorpe at it and he wouldn't touch it. Sent me t'doctor. Doctor sent me packing. Said it was a job for a man what does feet so I were stuck with it. Reckon I'll have to go private to one of them awful-pea-pick men what you call Mister and not Doctor. Mebbe I'd get down lane if it was cut. I can't get me shoe on. Cobbler said he'd cut me a piece out of shoe but I'd look comic walking down t'shops with it sticking up. Reckon it'll be theer while I kick bucket."

Now, while she was talking, I was weighing the job up. The nurse was kindness itself but very firm and was holding the old woman's leg tight and wouldn't let go.

"What's he going to do, lass?" squeaked old Molly in terror as she saw me produce my clippers from the case.

"The chiropodist is going to remove it, Molly - now relax, he won't hurt you. You're in luck today, Molly me girl."

I felt terribly cruel but it was no use delaying matters so we ignored poor old Molly's groans and screams and I got to work on the grotesque appendage. It was impossible to hurt her for the nail was completely dead. Six cuts with my nail clippers and I removed it whole. It was all over in the twinkling of an eye. Such a find was worth preserving and it would have been a crime to have cut it up into bits. Stubbins could write a whole book on that specimen. A few minutes filing and it was left smooth as her other nails. She looked at me as if I'd worked a miracle. I was the new Messiah in her eyes. She put on her best pair of shoes for the first time in two years.

"'Appen I'll be able to go jazzing at Darby and Joan," she said, in great delight.

I had made an old lady very happy and felt a glow of professional pride which, although I didn't know it then, was shortly to have cold water thrown on it. Anyway, I booked another appointment and collected the fee, plus a generous tip, not to mention a date for the next evening with the Irish nurse, to whom I had taken a great fancy. We are married now and every time I see an ugly toe nail I think of her!

Two days later Dick Cowthorpe called at the digs while I was still eating my breakfast. His face was even redder than usual and he looked anything but pleased. In fact, he was in a flaming temper and his dicky bow was all askew, which was always a tell-tale sign that he was ready for a row.

"I want a word with you, Mr Vose," he thundered.

"What about, Mr Cowthorpe?" I asked, apprehensively.

"About Mrs Thistlethwaite's big toe nail, Mr Vose."

"You mean the one I removed?"

"Aye that! You'd no right to see to it. I told her to go to doctor's as it were no concern of mine. That's not a chiropodist's job. I'm not covered for accidents to patients. "

"Then whose job is it? The milkman's? "

"Smart, aren't we? Bloody smart alick! Well, I'm not taking responsibility, see? It's your pigeon if anything happens. You'll carry can, not me, lad! "

I knew I was right and tried to defend my action. "But the risk of anything happening is far less now, Mr Cowthorpe. This toe nail was almost growing into the flesh. Much longer and she would have had a very nasty infected foot.

"You should have consulted me, " he said, thumping the table.

I looked him straight in the eyes and said: "I am a trained chiropodist - besides I got you a fee and another appointment. It was most urgent in any case. "

"Aye, all because a nurse gives you t'eye. After women, that's more like it. Let's have proper tale, lad . . . that's it, Mr Vose, isn't it? "

I looked at him angrily. "Right, Mr Cowthorpe, I'm not standing for that! " Somehow I managed to keep my composure and swallowed hard, then said quietly. "My private life is my own affair and, furthermore, let me remind you again that I am a fully-trained chiropodist and the idea of sending her to a doctor is ludicrous. It took me less than five minutes to do the whole thing. "

"Clever clogs, aren't we? " retorted Mr Cowthorpe. "And what's more, I've had cancellations because you've been doing 'em too well. Wasting my time that's what you're doing. What they didn't teach you at that flash school what you went to was first lesson any private practice chiropodist must learn if he wants to stay in business - always leave a bit of root in when you do a corn then it'll grow again. You'll never make a business man! "

"Maybe not, " I agreed, "but I'll gain the respect of my patients. This Onxychogryphotic nail should have been removed ages ago. . . "

"Onxycho me backside! Fancy names. All man and shirt, that's you. Head full of long words and nowt else! "

We were facing each other like a couple of bulldogs over a bone. His dicky bow was almost revolving now and I could feel the table shaking under my hands as I leaned forward and said: "And I'll tell you something further, Mr Cowthorpe, I've written a letter to Doctor Schofield about Mrs Millington's septic toes. I feel it's my duty to call him in. They're badly

95

infected and as she's blind I feel he ought to see her. She needs penicillin injections, I think. "

Whatever annoyance he'd felt over the Thistlethwaite nail, he was doubly enraged now. Beads of perspiration stood out on his forehead and he was having difficulty in speaking.

"That . . . that . . . blasted doctor! The one man I swore I'd never speak to as long as I lived . . . and . . . you . . . you . . . you send him to one of my patients . . You've overstepped the mark, young man! A whippersnapper of a student, still wet behind t'ears, telling me what to do! "

"But, "I argued, "he is her doctor. Surely an old blind woman's health is more important than a private squabble. The patient comes first, surely, Mr Cowthorpe? "

"In future, "he said, "you'll ask my opinion first, see? Did they teach you nowt? A few manners would have been more like it than all them big words. I bet you don't know what half of 'em mean any road . . ."

I had got a hold of myself now and sat down to pour myself a cup of tea, as if I wasn't aware of his presence. I could feel his eyes riveting into me as I drank with shaky hand.

". . .Just you ask me in future, see - think on, young man. There's others what would have this job in quick time, Aye, eggs and all. "

He glared hard for a few seconds then left, slamming the front door after him.

The episode didn't worry me unduly for I knew I was in the right and I went back to see Mrs Thistlethwaite that very same day just to make sure that the nail was completely free of any infection.

The more I thought about it during the day, the more determined I became to go up to his cottage and demand that Mr Cowthorpe provide me with proper dressings. Now was the time, the ideal moment. Even though I had stood up to him over the egg deliveries, I still nursed a certain awe of him deep inside me for I was sure he could turn very awkward if he really got worked up. I have always been one for the quiet life and avoid bother if possible. Besides, I was only twenty-five and hadn't had much experience of rows, but the one I'd just had with Mr Cowthorpe had served to give me much more confidence. So, full of determination, at half-past six, I climbed the lane to the cottage as I'd seen his red car go past an hour earlier and I knew he would have finished his tea. His wife blushed when she saw me at the front door. She'd obviously heard about the bother. I bade her good evening and said: "I'd like to speak to Mr Cowthorpe, please. "

"Dick, it's Mr Vose. He wants a word, " she called out.

It was most unusual for her to keep me waiting on the step and she was plainly embarrassed.

"Tell him I've no time - council business. " They were surly, grunting words.

There was no need for her to repeat them for I had heard them quite plainly.

"Then please tell him I'm giving in my notice, Mrs Cowthorpe, if he doesn't speak to me, " I said, in a voice loud enough to dispense with any go-between.

"Fetch him in't surgery, " her husband bellowed.

Ushering me inside, Mrs Cowthorpe said, "He'll not be two minutes. He's just having a shave - sit you down, John . . cup of tea? "

I refused politely and sat down on the operator's stool. Five minutes elapsed before he came in. I had reached the conclusion that this was a tactical ploy on his part in the hope I would cool down. I had, indeed, begun to wonder if I was being too militant. After all, I was a rookie and an employee. His gruff voice awoke me from my reverie.

"Grand evening, lad. I'm off council so you'll have to make it brief, " and he glanced at his watch.

I rose to my feet, saying: "In that case, Mr Cowthorpe, you can take my notice. If you can't spare me ten minutes then I'm not even going to begin to speak. " I was quite amazed at my reply for my resolution had begun to seep away during the wait.

He let out a great sigh of wind then resorted to blowing his nose on the red handkerchief, which was a permanent fixture in his top pocket.

"Well, what is it? About the words we had this morning? Well, you know how folks get het up . . . We're blunt up this part of the world, that's a thing you'll have to realise.

"No, "I said, "it's not just about that but while we are on that subject, I must repeat that I object very strongly to your remarks about my private life. "

His face turned several shades of purple.

"Come for an apology, have you? That's it, is it? Going to make me eat my words, are you? "

"No, Mr Cowthorpe, I don't want an apology, thank you. But what I do want are better working conditions. For one thing, this seat that's under me at the moment is most uncomfortable. I would like a real chiropody stool, and, what's more, I want dressings and medicaments. Many of the patients require padding and I just can't carry out the treatments in the

G 97

correct manner unless I have some stock. "

"They provide their own. It's always been't same, " he grunted.

"But I do object to asking people for cotton wool, " I countered.

He shrugged his shoulders. "Well, if that's what you want, I'll have to put prices up. Do you know what all that stuff costs, lad? It's all right you saying buy this and buy that, but who's paying for it? You wouldn't like it if I'd got to knock a quid a week off your wages would you? "

I shook my head without speaking, and he said:

"So it's not the brass that's biting you? "

"I am quite happy with my wages but I am very unhappy over the lack of dressings and medicaments. It is impossible for me to carry out my work in the manner in which I have been trained. "

He gave another mighty blow into his handkerchief, like the trumpeting of a bull elephant.

"Well, we'll have to think about this, lad, won't we? It's going to need thinking about is this. "

He walked up and down the room three times before he spoke again. "Well, how about a compromise? "

"What had you in mind, Mr Cowthorpe? " I asked.

"I'll get you a chair and provide dressings and felt it you'll deliver eggs. Now that's fair, isn't it? Meet me half way and it's a deal, " he promised.

"No deal, sir! The dressings are not for me. They are for the benefit of your patients and, ultimately, for your benefit, surely. As I told you right at the start, I will not deliver eggs. "

"Now look, lad, " went on Mr Cowthorpe, "Candidature for election's on in a couple of months and I'm up to me neck in't business. I'm running around like a blue-arsed fly, what with one thing and another and I'm getting right behind with me eggs. In fact, if I wasn't powerful on't council some of them fly boys would be muscling in and flogging eggs to my customers over my head. A quid a week extra plus dressings and anything else as you want if you'll deliver eggs and we'll overlook any broken ones, even ducks. What d'you say, lad? "

He slapped his hand on the table just as if he was in the council chamber. For a few fleeting seconds I was tempted by that pound - my resolution was melting again. I even felt sorry for him in a strange way. His face was beaming now, the glow of victory apparent in his cheeks. He thought he had me where he wanted me. Fortunately, professional pride came to my aid. If I agreed I knew I would be letting myself and the profession down so I said firmly, but politely.

"No, Mr Cowthorpe. Not under any conditions. I'm sorry but I would be letting down the tone of the profession."

He glared at me then strode out of the room, leaving me on my own.

Chapter Nine

Despite my differences with Dick Cowthorpe, in retrospect
life was sweet really. The people were warm and friendly and
I was becoming very much a part of the local scene. The
pedalling young chiropodist soon became well known and it
was common knowledge that he was 'walking out' with the
pedalling district nurse. Maire was the main reason I stayed
on for I'm sure only for her I would have handed my notice in
after the row over Molly's toe nail.

My relationship with Dick Cowthorpe had taken on a
smouldering characteristic. We tolerated each other and that
was about all. He hardly ever spoke to me except to grant a
reluctant 'good morning' because his wife nagged him if he
didn't, and I just paid him a cool deference which was only
right really for, after all, he was my employer. So as the
weeks rolled by, autumn was turning to winter, but those
Saturdays and Sundays still linger in my mind as some of the
happiest days I ever spent. Maire and I would set off in the
mornings and climb up the fells and over the hills with ruck-
sacks on our backs, full of home-made cake and sandwiches,
and flasks of tea, tramping hand in hand across the coarse,
stubble grass, to scramble over the dry walls of blackstone
which criss-crossed the fells in eccentric lines until they became wreathed by the ever-attendant horizon mists. It was as
if Nature was making a last tremendous effort to retain her
sweeter, softer side before showing her inevitable mean
streak of icy winds and snow. The tracks took us past isolated
farmhouses and smallholdings where we were always sure of
a cup of tea or a glass of home-made wine, if we were spotted
by one of the family. Even the dogs, which at first had barked
furiously at both of us as we rode our cycles close to their
private stamping grounds, would run out to greet us because
they accepted us as part of the scene. Lingering picnics which
seemed endless as we kissed and cuddled instead of chewing
our sandwiches and then the downhill walk to a cosy pub where
we played dominoes and darts with the locals.

As winter gradually set in and the snow visited the district with its deep drifts and blanketing carpet of frost, it seemed that this was a sign that springtime in my own heart was turning to winter also, for Dick was starting to get very ratty again and several times I was on the point of packing it all in. In fact, the weather grew so bad during November that I was forced to give up the domiciliary visiting until it became fine again. This meant that I did extra surgery sessions and saw more of Dick than I cared to, which was embarrassing for both of us, not to mention Mrs Cowthorpe, who acted as a sort of referee.

The decision on who was going to be the candidate for Dick's political party in the expected election was to be made on the first day of May. The result would not only decide his future, but mine also, and I was well aware that if he wasn't chosen he would no longer require my services. Besides, the practice wasn't large enough for two chiropodists and, even if he was chosen, what would happen to me if he didn't win? So either way my employment was in the balance. Still there was no news of a situation within the National Health Service. At least I was employed and that in itself was something.

Gradually, as I became more used to the situation, I started to feel that perhaps Mother was right after all. Private Practice it would be, for it certainly seemed that this is what fate had decreed for her foot-doctoring son. So I grew reconciled to what I then thought was the inevitable, and began to make the most of life as an assistant chiropodist because it seemed rosy in comparison to the prospect of working privately in my home town, a step I just didn't feel ready to make. And so, with my new mood of acceptance, there came a sense of contentment which was most conducive to my work and social life, which had taken on a more meaningful tempo.

This part of Lancashire is rich in characters, particularly amongst the Mill workers and Fell smallholders, and it was here that my aptitude for attracting comical and, sometimes, compromising situations had its baptism. It was not to be a baptism of fire, or of the traditional more usual type, but a classic example of the eccentric behaviour patterns of human beings which, Mr Stubbins had impressed upon us, were well worth our attention. How right he was, for just in the same way that 'from little acorns great oaks grow', from two feet there can arise a host of amusing situations, tailor-made for yours truly to become involved in.

Dick had several patients who, to quote him verbatim, were 'out of top drawer'. That is to say, they lived in large detached residences on roads leading out of the industrial towns and villages into the greener, softer areas of the valley. This was the type of clientele that he wished to cultivate - mill owners, civil servants and ladies whose husbands were 'big noises' in the city of Manchester. At the back of his mind, of course, was the thought that one day he would leave his smallholding in Barn Lane and move into the upper middle class society which he so envied. He did occasionally check my work lists and whenever he saw that I would be visiting one of these patients he would ask me to be particularly attentive 'for you never know when they can do you a good turn, lad'. What he really meant was that the prospective politician needs friends in the higher places.

Mrs Stackpole-King was the widow of an ex-Manchester property owner and lived in 'Fell View Lodge', one of several properties of distinction, to quote the local estate agency notices. As her's was the only double-barrelled name on my books I was at once intrigued. I had not visited her before owing to her being in bed with a heavy cold. When she had phoned to ask for another appointment Dick had only too gladly accepted and given her an appointment for the very next day. He warned me that she was rather absent minded and, once again, emphasised the need of particular attention.

And so, the following day after a long haul up the slushy road, I parked the push-bike at the foot of the path leading to the house. It was quite steep and still had a thin carpet of snow. I made my way slowly upwards through the garden which, despite its overgrown, neglected state, told a story of one-time splendour. The outside of the house was in keeping with it and the whole place had the air of decayed grandeur, a one-time rich man's mansion gone to seed.

I gave two knocks on an elaborate door knocker then stood back to wait and to avoid the water dripping from the gutters above my head. About half a minute elapsed then I saw a form crouch down in the vestibule. The letter box popped open and a voice said, "You'll have to come back."

"Are you not well again?" I asked, bending low so that our eyes met through the aperture. There was a metallic click and the door opened. I saw a tall, bent, sandy-haired woman with a green shawl around her shoulders.

"Who are you?" she asked, challengingly, her left eye slowly observing me from top to toe.

"Good morning," I said, "I'm the chiropodist. I work for Mr Cowthorpe . . . you rang yesterday."

"Did I? Oh, feet . . . well, it's not convenient really. I

102

can't do with folks keep coming - really I can't. I've had the plumber and the gasman already today and now feet. Come tomorrow, there's a good lad."

She tried to push the door shut. You would have thought I was trying to sell her encyclopaedias.

"I'm sorry, but that's not possible, Mrs Stackpole. I've got appointments."

"King, please," she corrected me.

". . . sorry, Mrs King."

"Stackpole-King," she said, sharply, "that's the name. Can't do with this shortening habit of the present generation. I've only had a bit of cold hot-pot since yesterday lunch - I'm in no state to have someone messing with my feet."

"Mrs Stackpole . . . er . . . King, if you are not well, it's perfectly all right. We can arrange another date."

"That's how we get missed," came the retort. "I've been done like that before by the district nurse."

"Well," I said, "I'm here now - but if you are sick. . ."

"Not so loud," she interrupted, "all the avenue'll hear you." She looked right and left around her, then opening the door wider, said, "Come in."

When the door was firmly closed against the thawing wind, she added, "It might not be convenient next time."

Still in the hall, she paused for a few moments, thinking deeply.

"Well, do them now then," she said at length. "They're ready for a going over, but the hairdresser's coming and I'm having bowel trouble. I might as well warn you. I'm real loose. I can't guarantee as I won't be taken short. Anyway, come into the music room, young man."

She shuffled her way into the front room where there was a very welcome fire burning in the hearth.

"I might as well be honest," she went on, "I've nearly committed suicide with it . . . doctor won't do anything and cornflour isn't half as binding as it used to be in the old days. I'll end it all one of these days, you just see . . . life's not worth living when you're old . . . but I'll have my feet done first . . . watch where you're walking, young man. It's all good class stuff in here. Outside's a tip, I know, but I can't do it these days, but inside is different. Everything here has a dear, dear memory." She flopped on a double bed with a sigh. "No fun getting old. Now, seeing as you're here, I'll tell you what we'll do. I'll sit on the commode while you do my feet, just in case - that way it'll save any embarrassment and you can carry on . . ."

103

I looked at her in horror. She was deadly serious. Then I looked at the commode - an elaborate, carved, oak contraption with brass straining handles. It stood there proud, grotesque and defiantly British. A tribute to British craftsmen, of British oak, and British brass, built to last despite the ravages of Old Father Time and senna pods.

"You mean . . ."I began. The very idea seemed incredible.

"It's the only way, dear boy."

It was the Egg situation all over again and called for a firm stand.

"Oh no! Mrs Stackpole . . ."

"King."

". . . it's out of the question. Completely out of the question."

Now I knew Admiral Nelson had said that England expects every man to do his duty. But, surely, he didn't include commodes in his sweeping statement?

"They do need doing," Mrs Stackpole was saying, "they're laddering my stockings."

"Maybe, Mrs Flagpole, but not on a commode." I was feeling confused.

"But what if I have to go?" she queried.

"If you have to go, you have to go," I said and, if I'd had any sense, I'd have gone too.

"Well, I'll sit here on the bed," she announced.

"And I'll sit on a chair," I said, glad to have got over that one.

"Wait and I'll get you one." She held out both her hands. "Give me a pull up . . . there's one in the back kitchen."

Ignoring the outstretched hands, I said, "No, no, I'll get it - you start getting your things off." I was being firm again.

"No, you won't!" she retorted. "There's too much fragile stuff about. People are so clumsy. Doctor Smith broke a precious vase one day getting a chair . . . give me a pull up there's a good boy."

Judging by her speed in getting from the hall to the music room, I would have had to wait about twenty minutes. Again, I ignored her hands and, instead, looked around for another seat.

"I'll sit on anything," I told her.

She muttered under her breath and began to undo her suspenders. Other than the floor, the only thing I could sit on was the commode. My eyes strayed to it. It had a polished oak top which turned it into a seat for rest periods. Strange, but it

104

even looked quite comfortable despite its hidden subterranean depths. She obviously mistook my curious glance in its direction for admiration.

"It's an antique, " she said proudly. "It's in the Antique Collectors' Year Book, is that. Those are real brass handles and those cherubs looking up on the legs are hand carved. There'd be a rush if I put it in the paper. It's an heirloom, genuine Waring and Gillow, and a collector once told me that it was the Stradivarius of commodes. He offered me ten pounds in 1948. Think what it would be worth now. There was one on that Antique show on television and it was worth seventy pounds. "

"I won't hurt it, " I promised her.

"You'll put a newspaper over it before you sit on it, and don't put too much weight on it. Think on, now! "

"If there's danger of me falling in, " I said, "I'll stand up, " the shaft of sarcasm falling from my lips before I could stop it.

She looked at me sharply. "No need to get ratty. Here, put this on it and then you'll not scratch it. " She handed me a back copy of 'Country Life'. "And put a sheet on the floor so that the bits won't drop on it. Genuine Wilton carpet throughout the house. I'm very particular, you know, and it's just been Ewbanked. And before you go, will you pass a toilet-roll over from the piano. "

I turned to look at the ancient upright. I counted eleven toilet rolls standing on the top of it. Four yellow, five pink, one red and one blue!

Maire called on her regularly to dress her leg ulcer and had warned me that she was a most eccentric person and it didn't end with her request to be treated on the commode. I have seen knitted tea-cosies, toilet-roll holders, et cetera, but never have I seen a knitted big toe 'cosy' before! And when I began the treatment she rooted in her deep black handbag and produced a most elaborate long-nozzled spray. For a second I thought she was going to disinfect me, then she turned it towards her feet and gave them both a liberal helping of scent. The room smelled like a Parisian boudoir.

Nevertheless, somehow, I completed the treatment which, I must admit, I tended to hurry for I was frightened to death that something dire would happen and involve me in activities over and above the call of duty. I mean, feet can be bad enough.

"Don't forget the toilet roll, young man, " she reminded me, sharply.

I went over to the piano and picked up a yellow one.

"Not that. It's a new one. Tell you what, pass that red one over. It'll make a change!"

I had the yellow one in my hand. My professional composure suddenly snapped - and so did my concentration. It dropped to the floor, rolling and weaving in eccentric circles to finish up wrapped round the carved cherubs of the commode. Strange, but I couldn't help but notice a look of abject horror on their faces as they peered up the legs at the body of the thing.

"Now look what you've done!"

Fortunately, the hairdresser arrived just at that very moment and she gave me a wink as if to say leave her to me, I know all about her.

When I visited her again we became the best of friends and on one occasion she asked me to stay for afternoon tea. I was then given the honour of viewing and actually drinking from her most treasured china tea-set, which had been presented to her late husband by a civic dignitary in the City. I admired her because she stuck so steadfastly to the mode of her former life of elegance though she admitted she found it hard-going and was 'as poor as a church mouse' now that all her husband's money had gone. All she had was the house and those memories . . ., and it pleased her to have an attentive ear to listen to stories of the good old days.

"I often wonder what will happen to all these beautiful things, Mr Vose," she said one day over tea. "You know, I've decided it would be a nice gesture to leave one of my best pieces to you."

I couldn't help but wonder just which one she had in mind!

Chapter Ten

I never did get my dressings and Dick was forced to employ an errand boy to deliver the eggs. In fact, things were getting serious 'down on the farm'. The fowls were producing over abundant supplies which was causing a build-up at the cottage. There were eggs in the cycle shed, eggs piled up high on the kitchen table, eggs on the ancient Welsh dresser, and eventually the overflow had to be stored in the surgery. The situation was so desperate that Mrs Cowthorpe asked me if I would do her a personal favour and mention to each patient that there was a special reduction due to over-laying. I agreed because I just couldn't refuse her. After all, it was only until the errand lad caught up on his deliveries and stocks became normal again. So at the end of each treatment I trotted out the sales speech.

"By the way, Mrs . . ., how are you for eggs? Twelve for the price of nine. "

The sales patter worked well and Mrs Cowthorpe would be waiting in the kitchen to complete the deal as the patient left the surgery. In time, the egg mountain righted itself and so I was never more bothered by requests to drop them off on my visits.

Though eggs are the first thought to spring to my mind whenever anyone mentions Rossendale, I will never forget the following April either. We had snow. No one expected it after the heavy fall in November, but there it was again, turning the valley and the fells into a christmas postcard scene when they should have been looking fresh and green with the promise of Spring. I was on my visits when it started, my third call of the morning to be exact. I was riding along, singing one of the current hits I'd heard on Mrs Sutcliffe's wireless that morning over breakfast, when all of a sudden the old Rudge started to buck and weave. In full voice and viewing the scene stretching across to the smoking industrial mill towns of east Lancashire, I hadn't noticed that the track had taken on a very rocky surface. As I slackened my speed to prevent my case falling off

107

the rack behind the seat, there came a hissing noise on the heavy clouded air - the unmistakable sound of a puncture and the first one I'd ever had. I didn't possess an outfit, even if I had, I am such an unmechanical person that I couldn't have repaired it and as I groaned inwardly over such bad luck the first flakes of snow began to fall. At first I thought it was a fluke, but more followed until, after five minutes of pushing and carrying the bike towards Smethurst's farm, the track was gradually becoming covered in white. I was going roughly in the opposite direction of Barn Lane, but I knew that Bill Smethurst would mend the bike for he was a tractor mechanic as well as being a sheep farmer. So slowly I pushed the machine up the rough track, stopping every now and then to blow on my hands in an effort to keep them warm.

By the time I reached Bill's place it was blowing a blizzard and I had to grope my way across the cobbled farmyard. The delicious smell of cooking invaded my nostrils and I was feeling so cold and fed-up that I certainly wouldn't refuse the offer of food if one was forthcoming. It was Bill's mother-in-law who opened the door, Mrs Ackroyd. "Come in out of weather, love, " she greeted me and then when she recognised me by the kitchen light, said: "Oh, it's young Foot Doctor, isn't it? I was only thinking of you yesterday. They're playing me up again. I'm not surprised it's snowing. I'll get Bill to make an appointment for me feet I said to meself. Well, sit you down by't fire and have a warm. It's as black as thunder without light on. I only hope we don't get blocked up again like'n November. Three weeks cut off we were. "

"Oh, I don't think so, Mrs Ackroyd, " I said cheerfully as I warmed my hands by the log fire and caught the smell of mutton broth with appreciative nostrils. There was always a delightful aroma of cooking in these little Fell houses.

"I hope our Bill's having better weather or it'll ruin Albert's day, poor lad, " she said as she threw more wood into the fire.

"Is Bill away, then? " I asked.

"They've gone to Albert's wedding in Leicester, " she explained. "Right posh do. All top hats and tails. Dropped on as our Albert. "

That was a blow. But the mutton broth was excellent and this was followed by cold ham and lettuce and a pot of tea. It was typical of these Fell folk to invite you in and feed you and then enquire afterwards the reason for your visit. I explained about the puncture but Mrs Ackroyd couldn't help me. She had no idea where Bill's puncture outfit might be and, in any case, all his tools were locked up. So I prepared to leave and went out into the yard, but the blizzard was in full fury and, already, snow was banking up against the house. As it would have been plain stupid to try to continue my travels, I had no option but to remain where I was. In fact, by four o'clock, I had given up all hope of leaving the farm that day. I rang Mrs Cowthorpe to tell her what had happened and she promised to pass the message to Mrs Sutcliffe.

The Smethurst's farm house was a cosy place in which to be stranded. There was the log fire and television and Mrs Ackroyd was going to make me up a bed on the sofa in front of the fire. I will never forget the scene as long as I live. Evening time and the crackling logs illuminating the kitchen in eccentric flashes which put me in mind of a magic lantern show as objects were suddenly revealed and blackened out by the waxing and waning of the flames. Mrs Ackroyd was convinced that to switch on the electricity during a snowstorm was dangerous. She sat in a commodious armchair, arms folded in deep contentment, while I treated her ingrowing toe nails, her feet upon my lap. I had offered my professional services as a little mark of gratitude for the food and shelter and in any case there was nothing else to do.

"I never thought I'd be grateful to see a fall of snow, " she said, as she filled up a white pail with hot water from the huge kettle singing on the hob. "A good steeping is what they need now and they'll be as good as new, " she continued, emptying half a tin of mustard powder into the water. The pungency of the foot bath mixed with the heady fumes of the pine logs to create an almost intoxicating cocktail which put me in a receptive mood for sleep.

The steeping of feet is a tradition in the north of England, especially amongst the older folk who spend hours with their feet immersed in hot water. But it is a fallacy that it works wonders; in fact, it has the reverse effect and serves only to harden the skin by extracting the natural oils. But you might as well tell people not to eat meat or take sugar in their tea - steeping has its roots in the mists of antiquity. Normal hygiene is quite sufficient as a rule, followed perhaps with a massage with an antiseptic cream or a dusting of powder, depending on whether the skin tends to be on the dry side or perspirant. Mind you, there is nothing like a good old soak after a hard day's foot slogging, as any ex-square-basher will tell you but, as a general rule, immersion in water does more harm than good. Several of my patients have told me that they steep their feet in vinegar. One actually claimed to do it every night before she went to bed. Her feet were hard and horny and gave her a lot of pain. I explained that the old-time bare knuckle pugilists used to soak their hands in vinegar for several weeks before a fight, the object being to harden them but, there again, the odd sponging with vinegar or surgical spirit is beneficial to the hiker or athlete because it does help to prevent the formation of blisters.

And so the evening passed pleasantly enough and we ended up having a hand of gin rummy with Mrs Ackroyd's feet still in the pail of water . . . steeping.

I spent a most comfortable night on the sofa and awoke to the singing of the kettle and the appetising smell of frying bacon and eggs. The weather was very cold with a biting wind whistling around the outbuildings like some plaintive dirge of a wandering spirit. After breakfast I braved the elements to find that the blizzard had created drifts which made walking a very risky business.

Despite the cold wind a thaw had set in during the night and the tracks were already awash with slush which ran down the ruts created by early morning tractors. Mrs Ackroyd assured me that to walk home would be madness and did her best to persuade me to stay until the evening by which time the tracks might be free. But when she saw that I was determined to make a bid to reach the digs, she came up with the offer of a horse. An uncle of mine had been in the cavalry and he was the only member of the Vose clan with equestrian experience.

Jonah was a rather dishevelled-looking old grey who seemed very loath to leave the warmth of the stable, but when Mrs Ackroyd stuck a lump of sugar into his mouth, he changed his mind and came out willingly enough.

The thaw was at its height and old Jonah was shivering and I was shaking too. It was going to be a long, slow haul. The picture postcard scene of enchanting, reindeer-land whiteness was gradually giving way to the grey, stark bareness of stone walls, bleak houses and the fall-out of industrial grime. But in places I could see grass and the greenery filled with hope, as if this embryonic sign of nature's softer touches was a booster to spark off a sort of Maytime in my own low spirits.

After a couple of miles, we reached a downhill stretch of road, and the old horse began to slide and skate. Mrs Ackroyd had told me that Jonah had only been to the blacksmith a couple of weeks earlier, as if this was an advantage to me. I jolly soon found that the new shoes were like skates on the slimy road. The visiting case began to slip away from between my knees, try as I might to stop it. Jonah just couldn't hold the road and at any second I expected to be transported head long into the snow and slush. I then did the wrong thing. Horsey friends tell me I should have stayed put and let Jonah do his antics all the way down the hill, but instead I panicked and pulled hard on the reins, calling "Whoa!" and of course Jonah whoa'd - suddenly, in perfect obedience! Visiting case went flying into a ditch, the horse's back legs went from under him and down he sat on his rump with such force that Mrs Ackroyd's tea cosy, which she had loaned me to keep my ears warm, fell off my head and Jonah and I were off again hell for leather down the slope. I shut my eyes and held on like grim death, the wind howling in my ears and such a strain on my backbone that I thought it would snap at any second. Then there was a sort of dull sound and a feeling of impact . . . then a minute's pause . . . and then I felt as if I was in a shower bath somewhere in the snowy wastes of Siberia. We were in a snowdrift which had not succumbed to the thaw, and this had saved us, but Jonah's backside had twisted and clouted itself against a tree. I was the recipient of every drop of slimy moisture from the branches and soaked to the skin. The horse actually seemed to be enjoying it and nuzzled its nose into my chest, the very epitome of the four-legged friend adored by Roy Rogers fans at our local sixpenny matinee when I was a kid. I nearly cried for the old hack, feeling very sorry for the names I'd called it under my breath on the nerve-racking descent. It was only doing its best. The case was back up the hill about sixty yards, so off I set to retrieve it and, by sheer luck, found it without any trouble. Then I had a thought. There was chocolate in it, for old Mrs Murgatroyd had given me some the week before, and I'd put it in the case and then forgotten all about it. I'd share it with the horse. No, I'd be a real Christian and give it all to the horse. After all, I'd had a good breakfast and poor Jonah hadn't had much to eat.

When I got back to the bottom of the slope I led Jonah by his bridle for a few yards to get us out of the snowdrift and it was then I noticed he was lame. I lifted up each leg in turn and on the last one found that a sharp stone had penetrated between the shoe, which was loose, and the hoof, and was pressing into the flesh. It was lodged firmly and any pressure on it was painful obviously. What would my childhood hero Roy have done? A quick operation was called for, so I opened my visiting case and pulled out my trusty nail clippers, just the things for taking stones out of horses' hooves.

"Hold on, old lad," I comforted him, "steady does it, old horse." Then I thought I'd give him the chocolate and while he was munching it I could remove the stone. I rooted in my case again and was surprised to find a piece of unwrapped chocolate. It must have come loose during all my adventures. I thrust the chocolate in Jonah's chops, picked up his back leg boldly, and stuck it under my left arm. My fingers were so cold I could hardly work the clippers but, at last, I felt them bite on the stone and pulled. The horse whinnied and thrust out vigorously with her back leg, but the clippers were in my hand and the stone tightly held in their teeth. I had performed the operation successfully.

Jonah was already looking happier, munching contentedly on the chocolate. Maybe now I could continue my ride. Then I realised I was feeling peckish and decided to have another look in my bag. Maybe I'd find some little tasty snack, for patients show their appreciation in various ways - apples, sweets, black puddings - and I more often than not put them into my commodious black case. Mind you, black puddings have a way entirely their own of letting you know if you forget about them for long. I was sure to find something to sustain me on my journey. Yes, a bar of chocolate with the wrapper still intact. But what was it still doing in my case, surely I'd given it to the horse? Mrs Murgatroyd's chocolate. . .? And then I found an empty cardboard packet. Good God! I'd fed Jonah a full block of chocolate laxative and he was sniffing in the bag looking for more - a dose guaranteed to provide horse manure for every garden in the valley. On the packet, in large print, it said: 'Enough for twelve adult doses'. No mention of horses. Mind you, upon reflection, I was glad I'd decided to play the Christian and hadn't shared it, though I knew I was guilty of base human selfishness. I felt terribly sorry for poor old Jonah, but did they work on horses? Enough for twelve adult doses - that would work on an elephant, never mind a horse! I felt an absolute heel.

"Glad thar's come, Mester."

I looked up sharply. The voice belonged to a tall, thin man in a deathless brown trilby and long, black overcoat which went down over his gum boots and almost trailed in the slush. A piece of string held the coat tightly round his middle.

He continued: "Jem rang up - I'm his fayther. You're a new 'un. Thar looks fair clemmed and I see thar's having trouble with your horse - a stone mebbe?"

I nodded but said nothing. Any horse would weather a mere stone, sharp as it was. But a dose of laxative, enough for twelve - oh dear! But Jonah still looked fit and was sniffing after more. I was so upset over what I'd done that I hadn't really been concentrating on what the man had said. However, he was saying just then: "Come on up t'farm and thar can have a brew before you starts on our Annie. Her foot's ruddy awful, poor lass."

So that was it, I thought. Annie must be one of the domiciliary patients I should have visited the day before. I badly needed a hot drink anyhow. After walking a quarter of a mile back in the direction we'd come, then up a farm track, we reached a large, grey farmhouse.

"Annie's in theer, " my guide informed me, pointing in the direction of a shed, "but come int' house first and we'll have a hot brew agin cold wind."

What a strange place for his wife to be, I thought. I was assuming she was his wife but said nothing and when we were in the large stone-flagged kitchen I warmed myself by the roaring log fire and eagerly took a mouthful of the tea from the pint mug handed to me by a tall, gangling girl. But if Annie was in pain then she must come before tea, so I said: "I'll take my tea with me and have a look at the patient."

"Take yours, too, father. It'll keep you warm while you're in the shed, " said the girl.

"Right, lass, " agreed her father. "Come on then, lad. Let's do job for Annie."

I warmed my hands on the hot mug as we retraced our steps across the cobbled yard to the shed, for despite the weather I was determined to maintain my reputation for having warm hands. "In here, " said the farmer, opening the door. Evidently some kind of a flat they'd made for the old lady, I surmised. Perhaps she was the farmer's aged mother. "I'll light lantern, " grunted the farmer. A lantern! This was a mediaeval abode. I made a mental note to report this to the Social Services. In this weather, too. As the candle spluttered its luminescence into the corners to disperse the shadows, I heard a groan.

"See theer - does think it's blood poisoning, Mr Coppal? "

I stared down at Annie. She was a brown cow.

"You've got the wrong man, " I blurted out. "I'm not Coppal. I'm Vose."

"But you're Mr Blakeley's assistant? I knew he'd got a young vet to help him. 'Appen you'll do, any road. You're a medic, " he concluded.

"But I'm not a vet - I'm a chiropodist, "I explained.

"Feet, isn't it - same thing? No difference is there? " he argued.

"Feet may be feet to you, sir, " I said, "but I only deal

in the human type . . ." It struck me, however, that it was ironic that having recently performed an operation on a horse I was now being called upon to attend a cow.

The farmer gave me a curious glance, liberally laced with disbelief, saying: "But you do horses. I saw you doing an operation on your own horse's feet so you must do cows as well? "

"Foot, "I corrected. "One foot - a stone. I had to pull it out - it was an emergency. I couldn't let the horse go lame, could I? "

"Well, what's this, then? " he queried. "Annie's in pain - so what's t'difference? You turn your hand to anything in country districts, lad. "

"There's a lot of difference, " I argued. "An awful lot, and besides you've called for the vet. He'll be on his way up. It's his affair. "

"Can't bank on it, " said the farmer. "Look at weather . . 'sides he's not reliable - and you're here and he's not . . . just have a look and give an opinion. That can't do any harm now can it, lad? " he asked coaxingly.

I wavered, "Well . . . but I don't know anything about animals. "

"A look won't hurt, " he persisted, "no' but a look. "

"Well, "I said, "just a look - then probably the vet will be here. " I knew I was doing wrong. I could sense it in my bones, but the farmer was pleased and said: "But sup thee tea first. " Then added, "I don't see as a cow's different when it comes to feet, even though they have four to our two. "

"I only said I would look at the animal, that's all, " I reminded him.

I 'supped up' as he had requested, then examined the foot. Annie winced. The leg and foot were very swollen and obviously infected.

"Very nasty - he'll give her antibiotics or the animal equivalent. There are wonderful drugs today. I bet you that in a week from now, Annie's foot will be perfect. "

"D'ust want hot water? " he enquired.

He had completely ignored my words and I could see it was going to be a hard task to shake him off.

"I don't want anything - for the last time, I'm not a vet. Fetlocks are not in my line. "

"If it were a nice bit o'stuff, you'd soon do it. " He gave me a leer and a nudge with his elbow and I'm sure he winked. "Aye, if she were a good looker, you'd do it, " he repeated with an emphatic stab of his walking stick. "Nowt surer. "

114

"If she was the best-looking cow in Lancashire - no, in England - I wouldn't do it, "I declared just as adamantly.

"I mean a woman, " he said.

"That's just the point. She isn't a woman, she's a cow." I again reminded him.

"A foot's a foot, man or beast. . ."

I could see that this was his theme song and there was no shaking him from it. For a few seconds he was silent, as if he was searching for some gambit, some persuader. He was, for suddenly he reached out and produced a bottle from a dark recess, saying:

"Warm theesel' up, lad. You're shivering. Drop of good Scotch this. I keeps it here for our Sarah don't like strong waters in the house, for you see Martha, that's my late departed wife, was strong church. Wouldn't have owt to do with drink or smoking. So if I wants a sup or a smoke, I comes here."

"Then you should have put your foot down, "I said before realising I'd only reminded him of his cow's foot by mentioning the word. "

"Do it, lad, there's a good feller. You'd not see a foot nagging and inflamed like that, man or beast. You wouldn't like to suffer like that, would you? " he asked as he poured the whisky into a cracked brown cup.

"That's enough, "I said, gripping his arm, "steady on, " The cup was three-quarters full.

He handed it to me: "Now toss it back. It'll warm you. Can't do nowt when tha's cowd. "

I took the proffered cup thinking that if I took my time and sipped it as I wanted to do, for it was fiery liquor, I'd be there for half-an-hour and he'd have plenty of time to nag me. So, I did toss it back. A sudden heat clawed with divers tongues at my innards. My groin felt as though it was being drawn through the lace holes of my shoes.

"Go on, treat our Annie's foot, " came the plea again.

I stood open-mouthed, but mute.

"W . . . w . . . ater!" I gasped at length. But I didn't wait for him to move, I just dipped my head into a barrel and trusted to God it was water. It was. I must have taken a pint before I came up for air.

"Another sup, lad? It's 'flu you're getting, " said the farmer.

I nodded and sneezed three times in succession to add weight to the argument. "Probably, " I said, "so I'll get off. I'll get back home by the fire. This is no weather to be out in with a cold. " He'd inadvertently given me a good excuse.

"There's nowt better than whisky. Why do you think I don't get colds? Go on have another, " he pressed. He kicked out with his left foot and I heard a series of glassy clinks. "Have another before you look at our Annie, son. "

"No . . . please, where's my case? " I asked.

"Case? Did you have it with you?" There was a cunning malevolence in his voice. The old farmer was boxing cunningly. "Does like fishing? " he asked suddenly in such a tone that you would have thought we'd been discussing flies and rods all afternoon.

"Fishing? . . . No, why? "

"Only that I own a lake. It's well stocked with fish. I was going to say as you could come up anytime you like - no permits or owt. Well, tell thee what, come up here blagging when September comes. And I'll let thee pick apples out of orchard then you can make blackberry and apple pies. . . "

I was fumbling about in the whisky-befumed gloom looking for my case.

". . .there's elderberries, too, " he went on ". . . about October's best time. . . "

"Please find my bag. " The man was becoming aggravating now. "I don't fish. Neither do I eat blackberries or elderberries and I don't do cows' feet - now can I go please? No ill-feelings and thanks for the whisky . . . and the tea. But, really, I must get off. I'm sorry for the confusion . . . I really am. "

I might as well have saved my breath.

"'Appen you left your bag in't house? " he said.

"Now look here, Mr Farmer, or whatever your name is, " I said angrily, "are you going to give me my case or aren't you? "

There was an undisguised grin on his face as he said:

"Perhaps it'll show up in daylight. Day's fair closing in quick. Listen, poor cow moaning. Bloody vet's probably playing cards in that golf club what he frequents. Bet your life. It's not fair when there's dumb creatures what need help. Poor lass. . . "

"Oh, very well! " I said. It was blackmail! I then remembered I hadn't finished off the tea. I drank it off and it soothed my burning guts. "Bring some hot water and a jug of cold. " I knew when I was beaten.

"Reet! I'll be right back. Hot wayter's always on boil here, " and he ran out of the shed, whistling in high glee.

"And make sure the bucket's clean, " I shouted, but he'd

116

gone.

I'd committed a cardinal sin against the animal kingdom by giving Jonah the laxative chocolate. Well, maybe this would square up the account. I could at least bathe the cow's leg in a pail of water and some antiseptic lotion I had in my bag. After all, I argued to myself, I couldn't do any harm. In next to no time, the farmer arrived with a pail of hot water and a milk bottle full of cold water, which I emptied into the pail and added a liberal amount of the antiseptic lotion, testing the heat of the mixture with my finger. It was just bearable. I lifted up Annie's inflamed leg and placed it in the pail. The cow howled with pain and did her best to lift it out while I held on like grim death, and the old chap lay across the cow's back.

At last the water cooled and Annie relaxed. The water must have been soothing to her foot because she stuck her tongue out and licked my face and I couldn't get out of the way. It was like having a wet shave with a wire brush. The old man was happier now and grinned at me over the cow's hind quarters.

"Like a human, is our Annie. 'Appen it'd break our Sarah's heart if owt 'appened. She's a pet more than a milker. By t'way, your horse is in kitchen. Sarah couldn't bear seeing it out in cold. She brings all animals in she does, though I don't hold with it. It were lying warming itself by t'fire. She thinks you're a vet and I haven't let on as you're only a shyropodist!"

With this parting shot he went off for more hot water to heat up the foot-bath. When he returned, he told me that the horse was fine and sleeping peacefully by the fire. I must have bathed Annie's leg for at least half-an-hour when a voice began to call for the farmer: "Mr Hepponstall, are you there, Albert?"

"It's vet," said the farmer. "In here, Mr Blakeley."

The door of the shed opened and there stood a fat, tweedy man with a bushy brown moustache and a red complexion. His gaze fell on me and then on the bottle of antiseptic.

"Who the hell are you?" he asked. "And what the bloody hell are you doing with this cow?"

Chapter Eleven

My first reaction was to look appealingly at the farmer, but he glanced away guiltily and said nothing.

"Well? " glowered the vet, his bulk almost completely filling the doorway.

I had to say something.

"Mr . . . this gentleman here . . . well, he asked me to look at the cow's foot . . . that's all, just until you arrived of course . . . well, I'll leave it to you now, sir. " My intention was to leave as quickly as possible, but his bulk was between me and the door.

"Mr Hepponstall rang up to ask me to come, so what you're doing here messing about, I don't know. Have I ever let you down yet, Albert? " he asked, turning to the farmer. "Now, fair's fair . . . have I ever let you down? "

"Oh, no, Mr Blakeley, " said the farmer hastily, "I were only saying to our Sarah how Mr Blakeley's never let us down yet . . . snow or no snow . . . Reliability, that's first thing as you looks for in a vet. "

"That's right, " agreed the vet, "twenty years on the job and I don't like anyone interfering once I've been called. "

"But I wasn't interfering, " I protested, still looking at the farmer in the hope he would come to my aid. But I might as well have looked to Annie, the cow. I tried to explain.

"You see, there's been a misunderstanding. Mr Hepponstall thought I was a vet, and I thought that he was bringing me to attend to his wife's foot, but then I found it was the cow's foot . . . well, I mean . . . it was the name Annie that misled me . . . " I dried up as he stared at me from beneath bushy eyebrows, a look of downright annoyance and disbelief registering on his face. I had to admit that it did sound a tall story, but I continued nevertheless. " . . .So to do him a favour. . .the weather being so bad and Annie being . . . well a sick cow. . ."

I broke off when he barked: "Well? So you're a chiropodist, are you? I've heard of you. Work for Dick Cowthorpe, don't you? Well, that's a blot on your copy book for a kick-off as me and him don't see eye to eye just at present. So you thought as you'd try your hand at animals, did you? Well, I'm tired of quacks in the medical profession and I'm not having any Tom, Dick or Harry trying to muscle in on the work of a veterinary surgeon." Whereupon he picked up the animal's leg and began to examine it, gently cutting away hair from around the wound with a pair of scissors. I wasn't letting him get away with a crack like that even if I was in the wrong and retorted:

"As regards your remark about me being a quack, Mr Blakeley, I think that a very unethical, not to mention nasty, allegation for one professional person to make to another. I am just as highly trained in my profession as you are in yours, or perhaps you are not as qualified as you lead people to believe? The least qualified people often make the most fuss, I find."

Now I shouldn't have said that. It was completely uncalled for despite the provocation, but the words had poured out in a flood of pique. Mr Blakeley stood up and glared at me with thunder in his brown eyes. His moustache was pointed at the ends and they quivered like sensitive antennae. To make things worse he was holding a wicked-looking syringe.

"You'll regret those words, young man, and, what's more, I've half a mind to stick this in your backside."

The farmer, seeing that a nasty incident could quite easily occur, tried to usher me out of the shed but as he did so, the door flew open and before us stood his gangling daughter, Sarah, her face flushed in agitation.

"Quick, father, there's great hunks of . . . oh bring the vet, father . . . hurry on, look sharp! Oh don't dawdle, father!"

"What's up, lass? Thar's all of a flunter, Sarah. . . lumps of what, lass?" her father asked.

The girl looked down at the floor then into her father's eyes, then she exploded with:

"Shite, father . . . great golloping balls of it - all ower't floor of kitchen. Yon grey horse what this young vet man fetched."

"Language, Sarah lass! Thar's not at home thar knows . . 'appen not proper. Company present, lass. Not nice in front of a gentleman like Mr Blakeley."

It appeared that I was not considered a gentleman in Mr Hepponstall's eyes, but then I realised that to a farmer a veterinary surgeon was bound to be of a higher status than a mere chiropodist.

Even by the lantern light it was possible to see Sarah blush.

"This vet, Sarah? Do you mean this young man? " asked Mr Blakeley.

"Aye, your assistant . . . aye, him, Mr Blakeley, " she said, pointing to me.

"Sarah, this man is not my assistant, neither is he a vet. Now tell me what happened to the horse but, before you do, isn't it a little strange, young man, " he asked, looking at me, "that a chiropodist, a fully qualified one to boot - should ride around to see his patients on horseback. Or did you qualify in Texas? "

"Well, " said Sarah, completely missing the sardonic thrust of the vet, "he came on it. I thought he was a vet. A shy-ropodist's no ruddy use to a cow. I mean blacksmiths do animals' feet. . . "

"Language, Sarah lass, "admonished her father. "Excuse her, Mr Blakeley, she's a bit upset is the lass. " Then he saw me holding the case ready to leave and placed his back against the door of the shed. "And where dust think you're off? If our Sarah's right, there's a lot of clearing up to do, young man. "

"I didn't take the horse into the kitchen, " I retorted. "Your daughter did and what's more, I never said I was a vet. You see, you both assumed I was. Isn't it time you said something, Mr Hepponstall? " I looked pleadingly at the old man but he studied the floor intently. Just then the vet took my arm in a vice-like grip and looked me full in the face.

"Well, as you can't go without your horse, Mr Chiropodist, maybe you'll accompany me to the farmhouse and give me your professional opinion upon the freak bowel movement of your grey. After all you are an expert on animals, aren't you? " he said sarcastically.

I could see it was no use arguing with this man who had made up his mind about me, but still I tried.

"It's not my horse. It's on loan. I'll collect it and then the two of us will leave and cause you no more trouble, Mr Hepponstall. "

But I knew I wouldn't get out of it as easily as that, and I was right for as the four of us crossed the cobbled yard, the vet said, "You shouldn't take animals into the house, Miss Sarah, you know. I told you before when the old sow burned her rear end toasting it by the fire. It's not the thing to do, so take my advice and let animals live in their own quarters, there's a good girl. " He talked like a condescending uncle.

120

Her father piped up, "She takes no notice, Mr Blakeley. Animal mad, she is. Good husband's what she needs and a couple of kids to cuddle up to 'stead of pigs and horses. "

"Father! " Sarah was shocked. "You know I don't like that sort of talk. "

"Is the motion abnormal, Sarah? " queried Mr Blakeley, his chin cupped in his right hand as he tramped meditatively through the slush and the steadily falling rain.

"You've never seen anything like it, Mr Blakeley . . . shite - all ower floor. . ." answered Sarah, full of relish.

We were nearly up to the kitchen door then.

"That's cussing, lass, " Albert said. "Unlady-like talk that, Sarah . . . bloody hell! Just look at shite . . . just look at it! " He swept the trilby off his head in a swipe of amazement. Even though I knew what to expect, I still received a shock. We could hardly get into the kitchen for it. And it was a big kitchen, and a good job it had a bare stone floor. Before our eyes was a rhubarb-grower's dream. A monumental manural mass. I felt an even bigger heel than ever when I looked at old Jonah lying prostrate and worn out by the fire.

"Copious! Quite copious! " gasped Mr Blakeley in professional amazement.

"Aye, and a hell of a lot of it, " seconded Albert, scratching his white stubbly hair in utter astonishment.

The poor old horse was worn out with its almighty effort. Then disaster struck again. The vet's eyes had taken on a sudden knowing sparkle. I could tell he had recognised the horse. After all, he had been in the district for many years. He proclaimed: "This is Jonah Smethurst, Bill's grey, " in a knowing drama-charged voice as he knelt down in one of the few clear spots on the floor and felt the horse's stomach. The old farmer and his daughter leaned over as far as they dared to have a look.

"Well, beggar me, " said the farmer, "so it is and Bill's away at his lad's wedding . . . summat mighty funny going, Mr Blakeley. . ."

"Look out - get back! " cried the vet, grabbing his professional bag in haste. He was just in time. It was just like the tide gradually encroaching on the clear sand on the beach. There was very little space left to stand by this time.

"This horse has been severely purged, " he said when he'd negotiated another clear place in which to stand, "very severely, " and indeed, from the tone of his voice it was obvious that he had made up his mind who the culprit was.

"'Appen it were at Bill's rhubarb, Mr Blakeley, " ventured

121

Albert.

The vet shook his head. "What, in April, Albert? No, this horse has been tampered with. He's had a dose of dynamite has old Jonah. Close that door, Sarah. Aye, lock it, lass, and put the key in your pinny. It looks to me as if our foot-friend not only treats cows but also horses. He's what's known as a cowboy and I don't mean the John Wayne type either. In fact, I'd go as far as to say he's pinched the horse and, as you just said, Albert, Bill Smethurst is in Leicester at a wedding." I saw red at that.

"Now look here . . . I've stood your insults long enough. This horse was given to me on loan by Mrs Ackroyd, but . . well . . . I did give him what I thought was chocolate. You see, it was in my bag and I didn't examine it first. I made an error and gave him a laxative instead. But it was entirely unintentional, I can assure you. I wouldn't hurt an animal for the world. . . I'm very sorry about it, really I am." I meant every word of it as far as Jonah was concerned.

Mr Blakeley uttered a dreadful oath and then said: "So we're getting to the truth, are we? I reckon we're going to have quite a tale before we've finished. Right, Albert, open Jonah's mouth. He's in need of a good stiff draught." He opened his case and pulled out a bottle which he uncorked and poured into the horse's mouth saying, "Give him the rest in two hours, Miss Sarah, and let him stay here by the fire." Then, turning to me, he said, "It seems you make a lot of mistakes, Mr Chiropodist . . . or are you as absent-minded as you appear?"

"Are you expecting more, Mr Blakeley, or shall we clean up room?" enquired Albert, holding a yard brush and bucket. The vet held up a large hairy hand.

"Don't you do it. Let the man who caused it clean it up, Albert. Open the door and stand guard. Get him a shovel and a brush, Sarah, lass. Reckon he should have his face rubbed in it, I do. Then perhaps he'd think twice about horse-stealing. He'll only get a caution, we're too lenient by far these days."

It took me twenty minutes to shovel it all away and wash the flagged floor with hot water and disinfectant. Despite the cold day, perspiration was pouring off me when I'd finished. The floor was like a new pin again and I was standing back to admire it when Sarah cried, "Look out, Father!"

Albert made a smart side-step, which nearly had his foot in the bucket. But nothing was forthcoming and Albert remarked sagely. "It's nobbut wind, lass."

Sarah had made tea and even I got a mug though this didn't please Mr Blakeley one little bit for he still glared at me with those fierce eyes as if he was in two minds what to do about me. It was obvious that he didn't want me to get away without some kind of enquiry into what my motives were. But I wasn't going to stand about all day, so I told him to ring the police if he thought I'd stolen the horse. Let them sort it out. Then support came from an unexpected source. Sarah spoke up.

"Why don't you call at Mrs Ackroyd's on your way home, Mr Blakeley? She'll tell you the whole story. I think the young man's telling the truth," and she gave me a shy smile which the cunning old farmer didn't miss and that computer mind of his translated the glance into what he hoped it meant. That Sarah liked the look of me. I'm sure matrimony suddenly registered in that calculator of a mind for all of a sudden he appeared to be on my side and backing up his daughter.

"Sarah's right, Mr Blakeley. Young fella's no thief. Give Dick Cowthorpe a ring. He'll vouch he's employing him. If not then get police up. I reckon it's a bit of a mix-up all round."

But the vet didn't see it that way.

"The fact that he works for him isn't in dispute. Dick Cowthorpe wouldn't know if he's pinched a horse," chunnered the vet as he sucked an unlit woodbine.

I spoke up now, "No, I'm afraid the only thing to do is to ring the police and tell them you're suspicious, Mr Blakeley. I am quite prepared to go with them to Mrs Ackroyd. In any case, I owe her an apology after what I've done to her horse. Let's get the whole matter out in the open and then you will see the whole unfortunate affair was a mistake."

The vet looked hard at the horse which by now was sleeping peacefully in the warmth from the fire. The medicine seemed to have done the trick. Then he gave me another of his fearsome glares and said, "But you'll not get away with your conduct, young man. Don't you fret! We'll overlook rest of it, but if you think you can interfere in the work of a veterinary surgeon, you've another think coming. God knows what you'll be up to next if you're not checked, eh Albert? What would Dick Cowthorpe say if I went round treating corns and Athlete's foot?"

The farmer opened his mouth as if he was going to say something further in my defence, but shut it as the vet continued his tirade.

"Fellar's a charlatan, a mountebank, Albert, and it's high time this unlicensed doctoring was finished. It's open shop for anyone in this country and if I get in parliament I intend to introduce a bill to make it punishable by law for unqualified medical people to practice . . . they can do untold harm, Albert. "

"I'd forgotten you'd got hopes in that direction, Mr Blakeley, " said Albert. "I know you'll make a reet good politician but we're going to miss you round here for't doctoring livestock. But I hope you get chosen for the seat. Just same . . . fill Mr Blakeley's mug up with fresh tea, Sarah, lass. "

The old fox had changed sides again and was gazing at the vet with new-found interest. It was obvious that the reminder of his political ambitions had set him thinking about just how useful knowing an eminent M.P. could be to a Fell farmer. Any ideas he had had of having a son-in-law had dissolved. I had only known this scheming man for a very short time but I couldn't help but think that he was the very man for parliament himself, never mind the vet or Dick Cowthorpe.

The vet's face was lit up by an ambitious smile. "Well . . I'm . . . shall we say . . . hoping, Albert? By the way, are you and Miss Sarah quite happy with the state of things up here . . . I mean water, rates and state of the roads? You've only got to ask, you know. "

Albert's mind was working overtime as it sought methods of putting the vet's offer to his advantage, and Mr Blakeley, in his desire to please, had inadvertently turned his back to me and I immediately grasped the opportunity to tiptoe out of the kitchen. When I was half-way across the yard, I turned and looked back and there was Sarah, giving me the thumbs-up sign through the window. All the same, once out of sight of her gaze, I hot-footed it down the lane, oblivious to slushy puddles and drifts of snow.

That evening I went up to the cottage, determined to tell my employer the full story before he heard it from other sources. But Dick was out at a council meeting and I would have to wait until the morning. His wife was most sympathetic and greatly concerned that Dick would fly into a rage. She started to make excuses for him, as she usually did, and I felt embarrassed and wished I hadn't called. But she needn't have worried, for when I entered the kitchen the next day, I was greeted by a beaming Dick, resplendent in new green braces and a yellow dicky bow, it was obvious he was in one of his rare good moods.

"Give lad a cup of tea, Freda. . . " Then he began to chuckle as if he had just heard some secret joke, his face like

124

a ripe tomato ready to burst its skin. ". . .Should have seen his face, lad! You should have seen it! Done you a world of good, it would . . . he were laughed out of 'Black Bull' . . . aye, laughed out of door and serve him right, pompous ass . . on his high horse proper, but they only laughed. . ." and he chuckled again.

"Who, Mr Cowthorpe? "I asked, intrigued.

"Who, lad? Why, that vet, Blakeley. Way he told story about you doing old Hepponstall's cow's foot fair had 'em rolling in't aisles - and him deadly serious and all trying to make it a council issue . . . it were better than owt I've seen in council chamber or on't telly . . . I've never laughed so much for years . . . here, give him a bacon butty, lass. Bike wheel's buckled and he's got no horse neither has t'lad. .ee. . ee.. I wish I'd a picture of Frank Blakeley's face! I reckon you did me a bit of good, Mr Vose, for he made a reet fool of hi'self, did vet last night, for it weren't good publicity for a prospective candidate to get laughed out of 'Black Bull'. No, somehow I don't think I've got much to fear from Mr Blakeley. " He put his thumbs under his braces and thrust out his chest. "Give him another bacon butty to put in his pocket, Hilda. Lad's got a lot of walking to do...ee . . .eee ... eee .. heck I wish I'd had a camera last night . . .ee ...ee, laugh, lad . . . laugh? " Dick was incapable of saying anything more for he almost choked on a piece of fried bread and a surfeit of laughter. He was still drinking water and having his back smacked by his wife, as I left to go on my domiciliary rounds. And I was laughing, too, and regretting that I hadn't been in the 'Black Bull' the night before, though in the circumstances perhaps it was better for me to have been well away from the vet while he was still in a bad mood over it all.

Even though I was pleased that my employer was more approachable and affable after the incident with Mr Blakeley, I was delighted to receive a letter a week later. It was from Blackborough Health Department, written by the Senior Chiropodist, Mr Evans, offering me a post with the National Health Service. Maire was sad at first but then she began to persuade me that it would be the obvious step to take. It offered security and the opportunity to practise my profession in the manner in which I had been trained. She had a good post at Rossendale and was very happy working for a local doctor, and would stay on there. After all, we weren't engaged and I was far too poor to have given any serious thought to matrimony even though I was very fond of Maire. Rawtenstall was only about thirty miles from Blackborough and as I would have to buy a car I'd be able to go over and see her. Of course, I was assuming I would get the job, so I wrote to Mr Evans, saying I would attend the interview.

As for the candidature for the election, neither Dick nor Mr Blakeley was selected, a complete stranger to the district was chosen, so Dick's dreams of political fame were never realised. Some while later I received a letter from Maire saying that she had met him in the street and he had bought her a coffee in the local hotel and had asked kindly about me and sent his and Mrs Cowthorpe's regards. She also told me that he was back once again working at that unique combination of occupations - treating feet and selling eggs and poultry. It was nice to know he bore me no hard feelings, and so my somewhat traumatic stay in the Rossendale Valley had a happy ending. I realise that I, too, had been guilty of working in two professional areas - those of chiropody and veterinary surgery - but I think it reasonable to say that my involvement in both had been of a high status.

Chapter Twelve

I must have made a good impression at my interview because I was given the job and so, once again, I was bound for pastures new. The train which had brought me from Liverpool was drawing away from the platform as I walked down the road from Blackborough railway station, my chiropody instruments in a black bag in my left hand. My only other worldly belongings were in a large suitcase in my other one.

I had reached the bottom of the station approach when I noticed a superb Rolls Royce parked against the kerb, but what took my eye was a beautiful dog. Its head protruded from the window and I couldn't resist it, for I am very fond of dogs. Mentally cataloguing it as one of those bushy Pekinese, I placed my cases on the pavement and fondled the animal's fur and tickled it behind the ears, uttering the usual doggy talk.

"Nice dog, good boy. Who's a good doggy, then? Hey? Who's a moochy-coochy. . .? "

But suddenly, it wasn't a dog any more. I was fondling a woman in a fur coat, her eyebrows bristling with indignation.

"What do you think you're doing, young man? " she demanded.

With eyes popping like organ stops and an urgent desire to depart the scene, I stammered, "I'm terribly sorry, madam. Really I am. You see, I . . . I . . . thought you were a dog . . er. . .madam . ." Now, in retrospect, I don't think I should have added that last bit.

In a voice heavily laden with damaged pride she cried, "Charles! Charles! "

I hastily picked up my cases and with her voice ringing in my ears I hot-footed it down the road. Out of the tail of my eye I caught sight of a tall, burly man in a chauffeur's uniform. By the grace of God he didn't give chase.

So much for my start to a new life in Blackborough.

Chiropody was now a very important cog in the great wheel of the National Health Service, and the Health Department of the County Borough of Blackborough was my new employer. As yet I had nowhere to live, and finding accommodation was left entirely to me. I would just have to find temporary digs, for I had agreed to commence duties on the following Monday, and it was already Friday and I had nowhere to lay my head for the night. About a minute's walk from the station I saw the Abbey Hotel which had a small sign hanging over the door with the word 'Residential' in black letters. I went inside. Actually it was a pub which did bed-and-breakfast but liking the look of it, and the bedroom when I saw it, I decided to take the room for a week, by which time I hoped to have found a place of my own because I certainly couldn't afford the daily rates of the 'Abbey' for very long, reasonable though they were. Bert, the proprietor, impressed on me right from the start that number six bedroom didn't have a key. To save him having to open it with the master key every time, he suggested that I leave the door open as nobody would go in except the maid who made the beds in the morning. This was fine with me but, alas, my memory has always been my worst enemy. I must have drunk at the very fountain of absent-mindedness when I was a baby for, in this respect, I don't think I have many equals. Though it suited my easy-going style to leave doors open and not to be encumbered with keys, the trouble was that I just couldn't remember to leave the door open when leaving the room. I would pull the door closed without thinking. Twice on the very first day I closed the door, and twice Bert had to climb three flights of stairs to open it with the master key, which was one of a tremendous bunch which bulged out of the pocket of his suit as if it contained half a brick. It usually took two or three minutes to find the right key and as he was a touchy man at the best of times this didn't improve his temper. Although he didn't exactly indulge in vocal abuse, his mutterings were pretty terrible as he climbed the steps on the third day of my stay, his fifth journey already that week. This time he actually pleaded with me to leave the door open. Meanwhile, try as I may, I couldn't find digs or a room anywhere.

As far as the work went I was settling down well and finding both the clinic and domiciliary work very interesting. After each treatment I would ask the patient if he, or she, knew of a room to let or someone who took in lodgers, but to no avail, and as soon as work was finished for the day I would grab a local paper and study the adverts for accommodation. It seemed my luck was out; there was always a snag. I followed up all the leads but when I did come across a suitable place I found that someone had beaten me to it. When I was lucky enough to find vacant digs, it turned out to be as expensive as the 'Abbey' and without the welcome advantage of a bar where residents could have a couple of pints after closing time. I was still surviving at the 'Abbey' though on the money I was getting I had to be pretty frugal in my habits. To make matters worse, Bert's nervous tendencies were getting me down. He was a quick-tempered, jittery sort of man, he lived on his nerves and I had the impression that somehow I was irritating him, apart from his frequent climbs to the third floor. My very presence seemed to be a frustration, for the point was that he didn't really encourage bed-and-breakfast clients. He only put up with them for the sake of his wife, for this was an extra source of income for her. I often heard him refuse people on the pretext of being full up when I knew quite well there were vacant rooms. One minute he would be all fuss and the next as edgy and off-hand as only he could be. After a week he began to ask me every morning at breakfast if I had found new accommodation. I had no alternative but to tell him that my stay at the pub would have to be extended.

By the Wednesday of the second week, my financial resources in dire straits, I struck a bargain with Bert's wife because things were becoming desperate. For a night's bed and breakfast I agreed to treat her feet and Bert's. They both had sore feet and had mentioned the fact frequently ever since Bert had discovered me stropping my scalpels in the Snug room just after opening time; so in order to allay any suspicions he might have that I was a latter day Jack the Ripper, I had no option but to put his mind at rest about my possession of such lethal-looking knives. But it didn't stop at just two pairs of feet. On the Wednesday evening, I found a queue in the kitchen. There was Bert's wife, her sister, Flossie the barmaid, and Bert's uncle Ted who looked after his cellar. And I didn't dare say a thing in case Bert took the huff and gave me notice. Mind you, he wasn't very pleased with me in any case. He was the last to be treated and I've never come across a more jittery patient. He pulled his foot away at every stroke of the blade, so much so, that as I was finishing the job by removing a corn from one of his little toes, my tightly-stretched concentration momentarily snapped. There was blood on the carpet and Bert set up such a howl you would have thought I'd cut his throat and not his little toe. The next morning he limped into the breakfast room and asked me if I had found a place yet, a black scowl on his face. My bedroom was going to be decorated and I would have to move out as soon as possible. He'd thought up a good excuse at last!

So it was no wonder that my absent-mindedness began to really assert itself. That morning I saw an advertisement in a shop window for a flat. Interested parties were invited to write for details. 'Ideal for Single Gentleman' was the eye-catching sentence. As luck would have it I had a cancelled appointment so I hurried to the G.P.O. and wrote a hasty letter which I placed in an envelope and stamped. My mind was racing. Bert's jitters were rubbing off on me. If I didn't get somewhere quickly I would find my suitcase outside the front door of the pub. With this vision before my eyes, I walked to the box with my glasses in my left hand. I dropped the envelope into the box and placed the glasses on my nose - at least that was the intention, but there was the envelope staring me in the eyes. I had posted my spectacles. My God! I must pull myself together - Bert was getting me down. I looked across the crowded floor of the G.P.O. The clerks all looked dour, efficient types. There was little to choose between any of them and if there was any humour in them it certainly didn't show in their faces. I joined a queue and quite quickly found myself facing through the grille a bald man in black, horn-rimmed glasses. Without raising his head he said: "Yes, please." He was studying a form and speaking like a robot.

"Er. . .well. . .it's about my glasses. You see. . .I've er. .posted them."

Lifting his head momentarily, he said: "Lost in the post, you think?"

"No. . .not lost, " I told him, "they'll still be there. I would like to have them back, please. "

"No, " he said, "you can't do that. Once a parcel is posted, it is the property of Her Majesty's Postal Service until delivered at the other end - sorry. Next, please. " As far as he was concerned that was that. He was studying his form again.

A large woman carrying an enormous shopping bag was elbowing me out of the way, but I held my ground and tried again.

". . .No, you don't understand. I didn't put a stamp on them, " I explained.

"Makes no odds, " the clerk said, not bothering to look up, "the poor devil at the other end will have to foot the bill. . next please. "

"No. . .I'm sorry, " I persisted, "But you've got it wrong. "

"Have I? " he asked, glaring at me. "Now look here. . "

130

"I. . .well. . .I absent-mindedly dropped them in the box. . . "I broke in hastily, ". . .not parcelled or anything. You see, I meant to post. . .er. . .this, " and held up the envelope containing the flat enquiry. The bald man stuck his head against the grille and peered at me, the big woman was bustling me impatiently and a long queue was building up behind us.

The form forgotten now, the clerk barked, "You did what? "

"I dropped them in the box instead of this, " I repeated, pressing the envelope against the grille. "I can't do my job without them. I'd like them back, please. "

There was an awful silence.

"You know how these things happen, " I added, as if it was an everyday occurrence.

"No, I don't know! " he barked. Then every eye and ear was directed to the scene when he shouted. "Charley, this chap's posted his glasses. Get them out of the box, will you. " His request was to a man some distance away, dressed in postman's uniform.

"Glasses? Specs? " He queried, obviously puzzled.

But Bald Head piped up. "Don't worry, Charley, you'll find them. They're not wrapped - now, next please! "

A titter of laughter ran down the queue. I stepped to one side to wait. A minute or two later I saw Charley hand something to the counter clerk. He raised his right arm and dangled a pair of glasses.

"Are these the ones? " asked the clerk sarcastically, and again there came the sound of titters from the queue.

I peered through the grille but in the shadow the colour of the rims seemed to have altered.

"I. . .think they are, " I faltered.

"He thinks they are, Charley. How many pairs were there in the box? "

The tittering was liberally laced with some belly laughs now.

"Thank you. They are mine, " I said hurriedly but, despite the embarrassment, I couldn't resist a desire to get the last word, so in a loud voice I said:

"I seem to have made a spectacle of myself, don't I? Good morning. "

Bald Head just glowered and my pun fell flat on unappreciative ears. I left the G.P.O. to silence and strange looks.

That same evening, at the 'Abbey', I was going down into

131

the lounge for a drink when a voice suddenly arrested me. I knew it well. Then I saw his face. The bald man from the G.P.O. was talking about me, in the middle of the story about the spectacles, no less. Hoots of laughter greeted his tale when he'd finished.

"Aye, that's him all right, Frank," said Bert. "He doesn't know whether he's on this earth or Fuller's. I'm like a ruddy yo-yo going up and down stairs, opening the door for him. Once more and he's out on his ear."

"Well, I'll tell you one thing, Bert. When I'm old enough to get me feet done on the National Health, I'll not go to him - not ruddy likely. He's such a dozy beggar he'd take your teeth out in mistake."

Frank downed his half-full pint at a swallow as if in emphasis to the remark. I didn't stop to hear more. I sneaked up the stairs again and got my belongings together then left by another staircase and out by way of the billiard room. Never again did I set foot in the 'Abbey', and that night I slept in the patients' chair in the clinic. It was very uncomfortable but at least I didn't have that dreadful door on my mind any more.

I found Blackborough to be a typical northern town, steeped in cotton mills, industrial grime and rugby league. The rooms 'Ideal for single Gentlemen' turned out to be a comfortable flat over Tomlinson's tripe shop. The final selection for the tenancy was between myself and an accountant, but I was cute and made sure that the Tomlinsons knew I was a chiropodist, for I had observed how badly they walked. If there were ever two clients for foot treatment, it was Mr and Mrs Tomlinson. So I have no doubt that the nature of my calling swayed the verdict in my favour, especially when I agreed to take them on as private patients. The unfortunate accountant had no such bait, though I suppose he could have offered to cook the books.

Tripe is one of those foods you either love or abhor, and I had always been a great fancier of the dish, but the fumes which somehow leaked their way into my flat certainly dulled my appetite for the product and I have never been as keen since.

So at last I was settled. I had a job and a flat. The feet of Blackborough were to provide me with many adventures and now all I needed was a car. My father had kindly agreed to lend me some money if I spotted a cheap car. It was the cheapest I could find, one of the first of the original three-wheeler cars. The type without a reverse gear. As I have never been a car-minded person I was happy enough and it only cost me fifty pounds and it worked! After Dick Cowthorpe's dilapidated bicycle it was like a Rolls Bentley to me.

My immediate boss was a Mr Evans. He had recently been promoted to Chief Chiropodist for the area, which comprised the town of Blackborough and surrounding districts. His promotion had actually provided me with a job because I was taking his place as the great majority of his work was now administration. I found him a very affable sort of fellow and eager to help and on the first morning of my employment he had asked me up to his office in the Health Centre for a cup of coffee. He told me that Baxter's Lane Clinic was to be my main clinic, though I would work the odd session at other clinics. What he was really doing was putting me wise to the set-up at this clinic for he had worked at Baxter's Lane for six years and had more or less become an institution. Knowing that I had only been qualified for just over a year, he impressed upon me that I must imprint my own personality in the clinic and not to take any notice if the patients kept mentioning his name.

"I took over from a chap once, " he told me. "He had been at this clinic for about seven years. I got to hate the sound of his name. 'Mr Jackson did it this way, and Mr Jackson wouldn't have done that. He would have done it another way', until in the end I met Mr Jackson and I told him about it. He said to forget about him. I was doing the treatments now, not him, and I must be firm. Gentle but firm, that's the secret, Mr Vose, and, by the way, you start on Baxter's Lane on Wednesday, don't you? " He flipped through the pages of an appointment book. "That's right. Well, if you want a bit of fun, John, there's a hatch in the surgery which connects to the waiting-room. It's a sort of architectural freak for the patients can't see it, but you can open it and listen to what they're saying. When they get to know there's a new man on, it might be funny. All the best, lad. Don't forget, just be yourself. "

I wonder if he ever regretted that parting remark?

He shook my hand warmly and I left the office with the invigorating tingle of curious anticipation in the pit of my stomach. It was nerves really for I knew jolly well he was right. Taking over from an established practitioner is never easy in any branch of medicine. New people are not accepted readily, especially by elderly folk, and it was going to be a real challenge to a newly qualified chiropodist to follow Mr Evans. Still, it had to be faced and so, on the Wednesday morning, I set out for the clinic determined to make an impression.

Baxter's Lane Clinic was a square, pebble-dashed building which looked as if it had out-lived its era. I parked my car in the road and walked up the main drive through the surrounding garden, carrying my brand new visiting case and feeling very important. I couldn't help comparing it with my last job when I had walked up the garden path of Dick Cowthorpe's smallholding to be greeted by the gaggling of geese and the clucking of chickens. But I had left all that behind and was now a member of staff of the N.H.S. which made me feel good and, I must confess, a trifle full of self-importance. I would be working in a real clinic and would be solely in charge. I was equally as fully trained in my profession as the clinic dentist was in his; I was an important cog in a Health Clinic, working in the same building as doctors and dentists and the knowledge gave me a warm feeling and made me just a little proud. But pride, they tell us, comes before a fall, and Blackborough has a knack of bringing people down to size with a thud.

When I opened the clinic door I found an envelope lying on the floor. I picked it up and read the words: To the Man or Woman in charge of cutting toe nails. It was a letter from a woman, cancelling her appointment. Then the door opened and a man in a brown smock came in with a cup of tea on a tray.

"Thought as you'd like a brew," he said. "T'other foot fettler always liked one, I'm caretaker, by the way. Old Cornflakes loved his char."

"Why do you call him Cornflakes?" I asked, intrigued by the expression.

"Because he wasn't too good at brushing up after he'd done, that's why . . . I hope you are, lad."

And with that point very truly made, he left me alone in the room. To him I was a foot fettler. I wondered if he spoke like that to the doctor and the dentist - inside two minutes my new-found professional pride had been somewhat deflated.

The clinic was equipped with all the latest chiropodial requirements - reclining patients' chair, the most modern of drills, instrument steriliser, magnifying lamp and a cupboard full of dressings and medicaments which showed that the borough of Blackborough was really up to date when it came to the care of the feet of its elderly citizens. I suddenly remembered that Mr Evans had said that the hatch was behind the curtains. They covered several cubicles which were used by the patients to take off their shoes, stockings and tights. After drawing back several of the curtains, I found the hatch.

I had arrived early to give myself plenty of time to set up for the session so, when I was ready, slowly and cautiously I opened the hatch. The voices of the patients were loud and clear. Two women and one man were sitting in the middle of a row of chairs. They were all well into their seventies. My list of work for the day lay on a trolley, and these three were patients who had come in a sitting ambulance. They were discussing the weather.

Now Mr Evans had told me to make myself known to the Health Visitors so, resplendent in brand new white coat, I walked through the waiting-room in search of the room used by them, saying 'Good morning', to the patients as I passed them - not a word in return. The Health Visitors were most cordial in their welcome and told me to make myself at home and to help myself if I fancied a cup of tea or coffee, and to dig into the biscuit box whenever I felt peckish.

On my way back through the waiting-room I said 'Nice morning' to the patients. Still not a word. When I'd shut the door, I tip-toed like mad to the hatch and was just in time to hear Mrs Hackburn exclaim: "Must be a doctor. They're going younger every year."

"He's new chiropodist, " was the taciturn comment of Mr Winterbottom.

There was a sort of gasping whistle as if one of them had a loose top set of teeth: "Yer what - new chip-opodist! " There was amazement mingled with horror in Mrs Hackburn's voice.

"The other fella's gone. He's over all t'feet in county now, " came Mr Winterbottom's reply.

"New man . . . never! " gasped Mrs Shacklady in unbelief. "He's only a kid. He can't have served his time proper. "

She made me sound more like a plumber than a chiropodist.

"Kid or no kid, he's new 'un, " said Mr Winterbottom dourly. "Like it or not, it's truth. "

"Why didn't you tell us? We've come with you for nigh on four years and you didn't tell us Mr Evans had left! " The way Mrs Hackburn expressed her indignation I thought I'd have a heart attack on my hands the very first day. Mr Winterbottom started to whistle.

"Perhaps he's one of them locusts that doctors get when they go on holidays, " chipped in Mrs Shacklady.

But Mr Winterbottom was adamant now: "I tell you Evans is over all't feet. I know a chap who knows him. That young 'un's new foot fellar. "

"Well, I'll go t'foot of our stairs," said Mrs Hackburn to the accompaniment of an angry stab at the floorboards with her walking stick. "I mean, it's not on. Mind you, it's typical of these days. They don't care about us old 'uns. Anything's good enough for us. They're only waitin' while we kick bucket. I mean, I've got veins in me legs and doctor says I've got to get proper attention every two months. I've been under him for last six weeks. I've been praying like hell for this day - Mr Evans knew my feet. They're not like normal feet, you know. I've got arthur -itis in 'um."

"And sitting in this cold clinic don't help them pains any, Annie. It's like a morgue - we'll all die of pneumonia," added Mrs Shacklady, sympathetically.

"What have I just told you, lass? Typical. We're only an encumbrance." Mrs Hackburn rolled her tongue around that word as if she really enjoyed saying it. "Encum - brance," she repeated, "that's what we are."

"He's only young, but he might be all right, Annie. I mean, we'll have to give him a chance," said Mrs Shacklady kindly. But Annie Hackburn was an ardent Evans fan.

"He's still wet behind ears - what does he know about my feet? You get used to one man and he gets used to your feet. It's a sort of familiarity."

"Well, perhaps you're reet, Annie. Young 'uns don't care about us old folks," agreed Mrs Shacklady, obviously considering that to agree was the easier course.

Her friend gave another stab with her stick, "I worked six in't morning while seven at neet and walked six mile theer and six mile back - Mr Evans said it was standing on me feet that made 'um sore. Ee, he were a champion at doing your feet were Mr Evans. I wonder has he finished doing feet altogether?

"Mrs Hackburn, please," I called out, stepping into the waiting-room.

Her face was as grim as death itself, but when the door closed and she stood in the surgery, metamorphosis occurred. Robert Louis Stevenson would have been impressed by Annie Hackburn. She was more of a Jekyll and Hyde than the character he created.

"Hello . . . I see we've got a new young man," she greeted me warmly. "I was only telling Mrs Shacklady that it was time that Mr Evans had a rest . . .Eee, that's what we needs these days, a bit of young blood."

Once in the chair, she proceeded to butter me up and praise the Health Authority, the ambulance service, and ended up by saying that the old man outside was a poor old feller with bad feet and I should have taken him first. In fact, she was most vocal in her praise of my treatment when it was finished.

That first day passed pleasantly enough and I got on well with the patients. As the weeks progressed Mr Evans's departure was lamented many times but they soon got over it, as Mr Evans told me they would. I just did the job to the best of my ability, and as the weeks rolled by, the name of Evans was heard less and less at Baxter's Lane Clinic. I really appreciated those few minutes he spent giving me advice over a cup of coffee.

Chapter Thirteen

House visiting has always held a fascination for me because you never know just what is in store. My very first domiciliary visit in my new capacity as a National Health chiropodist in the town of Blackborough, was to the home of Mr and Mrs Perrivale. And it is true to say that I began my duties with a song.

Just like postmen and insurance agents, I was to become very familiar with the great variety of door knockers which grace the houses of England, for often I would have plenty of time to study these highly elaborate objects as I waited for the door to open, for many of the house-bound cases were badly handicapped. The Perrivale's engine of summons was a beautifully polished brass creation in the form of a heavily-busted nude woman, arms akimbo and mouth agape, in the full flush of song. Underneath, picked out in red letters, was the single word 'Carmen'.

Mrs Perrivale answered the two knocks I had struck upon the diaphragm of the nude songstress and immediately my ears were pleasured by the strains of a waltz. Whoever the pianist was could certainly play well for there is nothing more grating to the ear than a badly played piano. Unless, of course, it is a lousy violinist. I am a music lover and this was to raise my stock immediately with the Perrivales.

"You must be the chiropodist, " she greeted me, warmly, with great charm, "Do come in, please. I do hope you like music. We don't have television and we used up most of our savings to buy a grand piano and a collection of sheet music. That's Mr Perrivale playing now. Nostalgic music I call it; he always goes back to the old tunes. We were on the 'boards' you know."

"'The Merry Widow', one of my favourites, "I answered, following her into the sitting-room which would be better described as the music room, for it was dominated by the most superb grand piano I had ever seen. Occupying the whole of one wall was a tall, glass cabinet full of musical scores and albums. Both the Perrivales were badly handicapped by osteo-arthritis, which more or less made them housebound.

Said Mrs Perrivale, "It's one consolation - it isn't rheumatoid-arthritis, anyway, for I'm told it affects the fingers and that would be the end of us, wouldn't it, George dear?"

Her husband smiled, nodding a welcome to me, and commenced to play a selection from 'Bless the Bride'.

"George and I toured in that show when it first came out," Mrs Perrivale informed me, sweetly, as I examined the badly deformed foot she had placed on my knee. The music was at once soothing and stimulating and my scalpel alternated between allegro and pianissimo as it involuntarily kept in time with the music.

When the treatment was over, George took her place in the armchair while his wife seated herself in front of the ivories. This was the regular routine.

"I suppose being young you'll like the pop stuff," and before I could say anything, she was bouncing into a selection of Elvis Presley numbers. Now this music isn't the perfect beat to accompany a chiropody session. My scalpel was nearly leaping out of my hand and I had to request a more soothing medley, otherwise Mr Perrivale's feet would have been severely punctured. By trial and error we found Ivor Novello to be perfect feet music.

As time went by I discovered that they both possessed fine singing voices, despite their declining years. George was a baritone and one of his favourites was 'The Boys of the Old Brigade', which he would sing to his wife's accompaniment while I treated his feet. He would never admit to being nervous, but I knew he hated having his feet treated for they gave him quite a lot of trouble. So the singing was a sort of cover-up but he still couldn't take his mind completely off what was going on at the far end of his body as he sang:

Where are the Boys of the Old Brigade
Who fought with us side by side. . .
Shoulder to shoulder and blade by blade
Fought till they fell and died!
Who so many and undismayed. . .
Who so many and true,
Where are the Boys of the Old Brigade
Where are the lads we knew. . .

And then his feet would quiver and his muscles tighten as he braced himself for the rollicking chorus:

Steadily we shoulder to shoulder!
Steadily blade by . . . ouch!
. .Ready and strong, marching along
Like the Boys of the - bloody hell! . . .brigade. . .
Then steadily shoulder to shoulder
Steadily blade by blade
Steady and strong, marching along
Like the - careful, young man . . .
Boys of the Old Brigade!

One day he said to me, "This dreadful corn on my little
toe has been the bane of my life really, but I still have a sort
of respect for it. . .I suppose it's pride really. You probably
think it's the meanderings of a senile old man, but you know
I'd be sorry to see it go altogether. You'll think I'm crackers,
but then perhaps all theatre people are a little eccentric."

"Oh, George, Mr Vose must have heard you tell that one
before," interrupted his wife, fussily brushing his green
velveteen smoking jacket with a clothes brush.

"Oh, have I, Mr Vose? Please forgive me. . ."

"No, no, Mr Perrivale, please continue. I don't think I've
heard about it." I wasn't just being polite for I couldn't recall
having heard this particular anecdote before. I'd heard quite a
few for, when he wasn't playing or singing, he usually told me
a theatrical tale, which I listened to with relish because I have
always loved the theatre.

"Well, Gladys and I were playing in Revue at the time and
I got too close to the Principal during a dance routine and he
stood rather heavily on my left foot. A corn plagued me ever
after. The man who did it was the great Jack Buchanan so I've
always had a soft spot for it ever since."

"Oh, George, how ridiculous! He does talk rubbish, Mr
Vose. . .really, George, "admonished Mrs Perrivale.

"But how many old troopers can say as much, Gladys.
Jack Buchanan was a star."

"But how many would want to say it, George?"

"Mean it, Gladys. It was at the Argyle, Birkenhead. I
remember it clearly as if it was yesterday. We were in
Revue."

"It was at the Alhambra, Bradford, George," corrected
Mrs Perrivale. "Oh, he does forget things, Mr Vose, really
he does."

"Couldn't have been, Gladys," argued Mr Perrivale,
"we never played that theatre. You know that."

"George Perrivale!" cried Mrs Perrivale, "And what

about that silly woman in the ridiculous red hat with the pigeon feathers, who kept sending you love letters the entire fortnight we were there? She always sat in the same seat; the third row from the stage in the front stalls - every night, mind you, and you tell me you never played the Alhambra. . .George, really! Pull the other one, dear. It's got bells on it. "

George managed a wry smile in the middle of a series of grimaces, for I was operating on the very corn in question. Jack Buchanan had done a good job. It was a beast of a corn.

Mr Perrivale continued: "I'd forgotten that, Gladys. But it wasn't there, dear. I distinctly remember now. It happened at the Empire, Liverpool, and don't tell me you've forgotten that pompous ass in the pin-stripe trousers and red carnation who, every night, did his best to push a bunch of white roses into your hands as we climbed the hill to the digs behind the theatre. I'll always regret I didn't give him one on his shiny red nose. I've had my share of bother with stage-door Johnnies, Mr Vose. "

"Oh, George, " said his wife, "all these years and it still rankles! Take no notice of him, Mr Vose - it was the Bradford Alhambra, whether he likes it or not . . . and that woman was double-chinned, and fancy wearing a stupid hat with a feather in it in the front stalls. . .I ask you! "

"The Empire, Liverpool, Gladys, " George persisted, "no doubt about it. "

His wife patted him gently on his bald head and made her way slowly towards the kitchen to make the morning coffee.

Before George had met Gladys, he had specialised as a solo performer of monologues, having made his debut at the age of sixteen in a concert party on the Great Orme at Llandudno. I can't remember all the monologues he performed on my visits, but I can clearly recall his renderings of 'If' and 'The Green Eye of the Little Yellow God' which seemed to be made even more dramatic by his cries of 'ouch' as I chiselled out that persistent corn caused by the dancing feet of Jack Buchanan. . .at the Alhambra, Bradford, or was it the Argyle, Birkenhead? The point was never cleared up although I visited them for four years.

One of George's hobbies was composing monologues and he often waxed sadly about the decline of the music halls, for he was certain he could have sold many of his creations to performers. At which statement Gladys would contradict him, saying: "Rubbish, George! They don't want that stuff today, dear. . .this is what they like now. . . " and she would proceed to plonk the ivories with great ferocity while she warbled,

"We're going to rock. . .rock. . .rock. . .around the clock tonight! "

Even in her aged infirmity the very essence of theatre oozed from her bubbling personality.

One day Mr Perrivale said that he was so grateful for the comfort I gave them both that he wanted to write a monologue for me. Had I any humorous stories about my profession? So I told him about the time I had visited Mrs Stackpole-King in Rossendale and the saga of the commode. The old singer was quite amused and promised to let his imagination loose on the subject and present me with the result on my next visit. Sure enough he kept his promise and I was treated to the following rendering, which he had written on a page of an exercise book and which I have kept ever since:

An Ode to a Commode
(with apologies to Hayes and Kipling)

There's an ancient brown commode due east of Burnley town
There's a rather loose old lady standing by.
Her lover died of poison in a tent in Katmandu
"Never leave your posts! " was his last cry.
His message came by Corporal who had to change at Crewe
His awful news was dire, but Queenie did not cry,
Instead she got the looseness, this was her sorrowful load.
And never another laxative did she buy.
She is doing it for England when she uses the commode
And in memory of her sweetheart, Captain Fry.

And now in modern Burnley, where you gets your feet done
free
A chiropodial gentleman came by.
He was as British as the Captain, with his scalpels made of
steel!
But when Queenie propositioned he was shy.
He had fought the dreaded bunion in climates hot and cold.
He never flinched, his motto do or die,
But each man has his limit, and his was the commode,
Than do her feet on that he'd sooner die!
But when Queenie goes to heaven and meets her Captain Dear
And his Jack-of-all-Trades Wallah over gin,
He'll do her corns by blowpipe as she sits on the commode
For you're a braver man than I am - Gunga Din!

That was the last time I was to see the delightful couple for they both died four weeks later, only three days separating their deaths. And afterwards, whenever I drove around the corner past the music room, I seemed to hear their voices in sweet duet:

". . .Blue heaven and you and I. .The sand kissing the Moonlit sky. . .The desert breeze. . ."

Though I had only known them as an old couple, I had no trouble in picturing them as a handsome, romantic, leading man and a petite, vivacious leading lady.

Such visits are the highspots in a working life and domiciliary visiting does lend great variety to a chiropodist's work. Variety, so they tell us, is the spice of life and it seemed Fate had in store for me plenty of this spice.

Every morning I received a list of the day's work and as the cases were all new to me the names meant nothing then. A Mrs Alice Blenkinsop was down for a house visit during my second week. When I arrived at her terraced house, I noticed that the curtains were drawn even though it was three o'clock in the afternoon. I knocked on the door and immediately there was a shrill "Who is it?" in response. I opened the letter box and called out: "Chiropodist."

"Oh, feet," came the reply, "I don't think it's convenient today."

"Didn't you get a card to let you know I was coming?" I asked through the aperture in the letter box. There was no answer except heavy breathing. I could almost hear her brain working though I couldn't see her. Then there was a click and the door opened ever so slowly. I could see one eye peering at me, looking me up and down.

"Well, come in," she said at last after great deliberation. "They do need doing. Come in, Mister."

I knew from the treatment card that this was the first time a chiropodist had visited the house. The hall was dingy and there was a heavy museum sort of smell and, even though it was a summer's day, only a few rays of light penetrated the gloom. Although I had been invited inside, the woman seemed loath to let me go any further, as if she was having second thoughts.

"They'll wait, lad. Leave it until next time, will you?"

"If your feet are hurting you," I said, "it's best to have them done now, Mrs Blenkinsop. You'll be glad. . .it won't take long."

"Perhaps you're right, lad. I've got nails like cats' claws and I've a corn what would win prizes in Blackborough Festival. Come on int'parlour then. As you say, it's for t'best. Private

143

chiropodists are all booked up so better do it now. "

The parlour was very dark also and, judging by the difficulty I had in opening the curtains, they hadn't been disturbed for many a long day. Daylight was indeed a stranger to that room.

When she was seated comfortably in an armchair, I began the treatment. Her feet were in a badly neglected state and in dire need of chiropody treatment. Old Alice almost went into a trance, perfectly at ease, whilst I worked away at the task of making her feet comfortable and presentable once more. When the left foot treatment was completed, she suddenly came to life again and started to put her stocking on.

"Put the other one up now, Mrs Blenkinsop, please. "

She shook her head. "You'll have to excuse me, young man. I've got dinner put in t'oven. My Fred and our Bob will be in at five. It'll only take me five minutes. Then it'll be cooking while you do my other foot. It's all ready for the oven. "

Though I was anxious to get on with the job, for I had two more patients to attend, I didn't object as this was the first visit to Mrs Blenkinsop. She shuffled away and shortly I could hear the rattle of pots and pans. After about five minutes, she returned, carrying a cup and saucer.

"I thought as foot man'd like a brew so I've brought you a cup of tea. You'll find sugar ont' mantelpiece. Help yourself. You will if you're anything like my Fred and our Bob. They love sugar, real sweet tooths they are. " She placed the cup and saucer on the table next to me and once more sat down in the armchair for the second half of the treatment. "You might meet Fred - that's me husband - and the lad, Bob. You'll like him. Both tall, like you, they are. My Fred's got sore feet. I keep telling him he could do with 'um doing. His nails scratch me in bed, they do. "

"Why doesn't he have them treated at the clinics? " I asked.

"Good idea, lad. I'll get him to make an appointment at t'health centre. Or perhaps you'd do 'um for him if he comes in now. I'll make more tea for you while you wait. "

"It's kind of you, " I said, "but I must be on my way and, I'm sorry, but your husband must have an appointment, Mrs Blenkinsop. "

She then started to tell me how much better her feet were feeling and said that she appreciated my visit so much that she would feel happier if I accepted some of her homemade mince pies. She made them for her Fred every week and had

144

done since they were first married, so I thanked her and accepted the gift. At the door she thanked me again, profusely, and waved to me as I opened the car door.

"They feel lovely now, thanks," she called out, then closed the door.

Just then I caught sight of a woman's head in a hair net, peering at me over the hedge of the next garden.

"Just a minute. You!"

I looked round again. It was the woman calling to me and her tone of voice was very fierce. "Do you want me?" I enquired, rather irritated by her brusque manner.

"Yes," she said, "who are you?" and once more the tone was calculated to put the back up of even the mildest of men.

"I beg your pardon?" I said, slowly.

"You. Who are you? What are you doing next door?" she repeated.

"And who are you for that matter, may I ask?" The question seemed to melt her fierceness.

"Don't mind me," she apologised. "Sorry I snapped at you. It's just that you came out of Mrs Blenkinsop's next door."

"That's right," I said. "I'm the chiropodist. Mrs Blenkinsop is one of my patients and I'm from the Health Centre."

"But how did you get in?"

"In the normal way. She opened the door and let me in. Mind you, she was a trifle strange at first."

"Strange?" she echoed. "That's putting it mildly. Do you know, she's not let anyone past the door for years. Her feet must have been bad that's all I can say. Did she act queer, sort of peculiar?"

"Not really." I said, "but she did get up to put her husband's and son's tea in the oven half way through the treatment."

She gripped my arm at that. "Did she say anything about them?" I could feel her bony fingers biting into my flesh even though I had on a jacket.

"She did ask me to wait until they came in so I could attend to her husband's feet."

"It's as well you didn't, luv." said the woman, "they're past having their feet done, God rest them both. They were both killed in a pit disaster seven years ago."

So it was little wonder that during my stint in Blackborough I soon became quite famous amongst my colleagues because of my adventures involving patients. Mind you, I have always seemed to attract strange happenings, just like a magnet attracts metal. In reality, however, it was just the drop of the cards, because the work was given out by the clerks at the Health Centre. The fact was that by some freak I seemed to be given the most unusual ones. Like the time I had a Mrs Unsworth down on my domiciliary list for a Friday afternoon visit.

I had decided to leave her until the last one because it was the nearest call to my flat. The afternoon was very hot when I knocked on the door at four o'clock and I noticed that in spite of the heat the curtains were drawn, both upstairs and down. People had told me during my travels that bright sunlight faded carpets, so I assumed that this was why the curtains were drawn.

A youngish woman answered the door, "Come in, please."

As it was obvious I was expected, I didn't think it necessary to go through my usual routine of introducing myself.

"She's in this room," continued the woman.

"Hullo, Mrs Unsworth," I said, although I couldn't see her in the room as my eyes had not accustomed themselves to the gloom.

The woman who had answered the door said, "I beg your pardon," and gave me a strange look.

"I thought the lady was in here," I explained, "but I see now that she isn't. If you will bring her in, I'll set out my instruments and I'd like a towel to put over my knees, please, and perhaps a couple of sheets of newspaper on the floor to protect the carpet."

"But my mother is here, Mr. . ."

"Vose," I informed her.

She gave me another strange look as she saw me looking round the room for the patient.

"Behind the screen, Mr Vose," she said. "Wait, I'll draw the curtains then you can see properly."

Daylight flooded in and I saw an ancient screen. I was becoming used to performing my duty in all sorts of strange circumstances, so I wasn't surprised.

"Well, I suppose I can work behind it. There's plenty of light from the window. . . don't want to cut any toes off, do we. . .hah. . .hah!"

My flippancy wasn't going down at all well. Most people joke about their feet but my patient's daughter had her mouth open. There was a look of unbelief on her face. She was obviously flabbergasted and didn't share my humour which I must admit wasn't very funny.

"Just who are you?" she asked, slowly.

"The chiropodist," I said, "who were you expecting?"

146

She dropped on to the armchair and buried her face in her hands.

"Oh, my God! I told Jack to cancel my mother's appointment. She's dead, behind the screen. I thought you were from the coroner's office. To think, she was going mad to have her feet done last week - what a pity."

Chapter Fourteen

Amongst a host of literary works, G.K. Chesterton is credited with the immortal aphorism, 'Any man who can look at his feet without laughing has no sense of humour'. Feet have always been regarded as good for a laugh, a stock subject for comedians, yet I have come across many hundreds of people who do just the opposite, they moan and groan about their feet. But despite the pain they cause us we still laugh at feet, for paradoxical though this may seem, my familiarity has not dampened my appreciation of the humour produced by these overworked anatomical structures: I still find that feet are funny.

The humour of chiropody, in common with most other types, can roughly be divided into the unconscious and the contrived. Outrageous remarks are not as uncommon as one might imagine and I have been given many a laugh by patients who get into difficulty with big words. Like the elderly gentleman who stopped me in the corridor one day and enquired where he could ask a hypotesticle question about his feet. Rare as such a remark might be, chiropodists everywhere must be familiar with the patient who says that her feet only hurt when she stands on them, whilst others think they are extra special cases judging by the remark, "You know, Mr Vose, I've walked on my feet all my life." And from the tone of voice in which this information is divulged it would appear that the rest of us spend our time crawling about on hands and knees. A wonderfully intriguing picture of separate beds is conjured up by the remark, "I don't sleep with my feet at night any more", and it is no longer original to be told by a patient that there's nothing wrong with her feet, it's her toe nails that are the culprits.

Not that all unconscious humour is concerned with feet, for the chiropodist is a captive audience for the patient who wants to impart confidential and, sometimes, intimate revelations. Cne day I was asked for aspirins to relieve the pain of nostalgia in the buttocks; and one day a man told me that he was going to have his probate gland removed! I couldn't help but wonder if he would be attending the local hospital or a solicitor's office to have the job done.

Continual discussion about feet can become a trifle boring day after day, so reference to general health can make a change - though the risk of being on the receiving end of a recital of complaints, ranging from rheumatism to dandruff, is ever attendant.

"How am I?" said Mrs Chadwick in reply to my enquiry, "Not well at all." Then, bending down nearer to my right ear, whispered, "You're a married man, aren't you, Mr Vose?" I assured her I was. "Well, you'll understand then. . . you see I've had one of them women's operations. They took everything away - everything. . .a woman's never the same after in health when they've done that." She paused for a second to sigh about the sadness of old age, then added, "They call it an hysterical rectum."

To walk along the corridors of the clinic dressed in a white coat was to invite queries from people wandering about in search of various departments.

"Can you help me, doctor?" A fur-clad lady greeted me in the main hall one morning.

"I'll do my best," I said, not displeased at the ego-boosting mode of address.

"You see, I've come for a surgical spear, doctor. Where do I go?"

Now, to have shown my ignorance and tell her that I didn't know what the dickens a surgical spear was, would have been letting the image down, so after a few seconds thought I plumped for the surgical appliance department, where such sundry items as bed-pans, hoists and commodes were handed out on loan. Though the description sounded more like a sophisticated Zulu assegai, I assumed that it must be some sort of appliance unknown to me. She thanked me and went off down the corridor. About an hour later my surgery phone rang. It was one of the nursing officers.

"Did you send a lady to appliances earlier this morning?" she enquired, and I sensed good humour in her voice. "She said it was a tall man in a white coat, so I knew it must be you."

"Yes," I said.

She started chuckling, "Well, I thought I'd let you know that she eventually ended up with me."

"I must say," I confessed, "I've never heard of a surgical spear. What did she want?"

For a few seconds the phone was alive with giggling noises and background chuckles ". . .a cervical smear! " she managed to say at last.

Another phone call I received had me tingling with anticipation for the voice was soft, sensuous and definitely female. "Is that you, Mr Vose? " It purred in the silky tones of one of those continental nightclub singers portrayed on the screen by Miss Marlene Dietrich. And when it went on to purr "I want to see you urgently. I've got information in my big toe, " - for a second I thought I had been contacted by some latter day Mata Hari, but my delusions were shattered when I recognised the voice as belonging to the chronically laryngitic Mrs Sidebottom, who was nearer seventy than sixty, and well known to me for getting into difficulties with big words.

Mrs Dodds always blamed her ancestors for her bad feet. "I've got my mother's feet, so has my brother as well, " she told me. 'A foot each? ' I was tempted to ask, but thought better of it when she went on to explain, "Genital bunions, both of us. "

There have been times when I've felt more like a parish priest than a chiropodist. A most embarrassed lady one day whispered into my ear in a confessional voice, making me promise not to tell any of her friends what she said. It was my first day back at work after the Christmas holidays and she had come hobbling into the clinic in great pain. She told me that she had got tipsy at a party and was dancing in her bare feet when it was discovered that the nut-crackers were missing. Without more ado, fortified by an excess of Christmas Spirit, she stamped on a cashew nut with all her might. The nut didn't break, but her foot did. I called at her house that same evening to hear the hospital verdict; x-rays had revealed two fractured metatarsus. And I thought she added a nice touch to the incident by saying, "I'm the one who's nuts, Mr Vose. "

I will never forget Mrs Smallman either, for she came into the surgery in such a meek and mild way that I assumed she must be very nervous.

"You're a new man, aren't you? " she asked me, in a tone of voice which told me that she knew very well I was a new-comer, so there was no need to answer. So that was it. She didn't like changes.

"Oh dear! Just when I'd got used to Mr Evans . . . to go through all that again . . . oh dear. "

"Through what, Mrs Smallman? " I asked.

"Oh, it's not me feet - at least, I mean, it's not that I'm worried about you doing 'em - in fact, I've heard good reports

150

of you - no, it's. . .well. . .it's very embarrassing really. In fact, I wanted Mr Evans to take me on privately, but he wouldn't." She was looking at me pleadingly. "Promise not to say a word to the others in the club. . .the Cons. You know. . they all come here. Scout's honour?"

"Scout's honour," I said reassuringly, "but, Mrs Smallman, anything you tell me, or show me for that matter, is private and won't go any further. Besides chiropodists are used to seeing all kinds of feet."

"They can always learn, love," she said from behind the curtain as she took off her stockings. "Ah well. . .here goes." She sighed resignedly as she placed her feet on the foot rest, saying: "Laugh if you want to. . .Mr Evans did, the cheeky monkey."

I hadn't known what to expect and found myself gazing in astonishment at two tattooed feet! I was too polite to laugh and said the first thing that came into my head, "Didn't it hurt you, Mrs Smallman? I mean, it must have been like a Chinese torture." The tattooing had been done on the top surface of both feet and almost covered the space between the base of the toes and the bend of the ankle.

"The heart with the arrow through it on my left hurt for days after but it was in my wild youth, and you do some stupid things when you're young and in love. You see, I went head-over-heels for a fairground tattooist, against me parent's wishes. Mind you, they were right, and I'm glad it never got to marriage. He was too fond of the drink for me. Of course I was headstrong and wouldn't listen to advice. He wanted to tattoo me as a memento I could keep all me life. I wanted to but knew Mum and Dad would go mad, so in the end I let him do it on me feet and, do you know, I kept it a secret from my parents. In fact, only three or four people have seen them in forty-five years."

I cannot say that I have ever been fond of tattooes, but I must admit that 'Love will never die', edged in red by trailing roses, on her right foot, was indeed a masterpiece of the art.

There are some patients, rare I'm glad to say, who make a practice of getting a laugh at the chiropodist's expense. Like Joe Wotherspoon, for example. Joe was a resident in a Home for senior citizens in the town and it was part of my duties to treat the residents' feet periodically. On my very first visit Joe dangled the bait and I took it like a gullible cod, and the hook, line and sinker. Some of the handicapped people wheeled themselves around the home in chairs and Joe was one who could speed around the corridors like a racing driver. On the second day of my visit I met him in the hall and he was coming towards me at great speed. For a second I thought he was going to knock me down, but suddenly he braked, did a three-point turn, then came up alongside me as I was walking towards the doctor's room, a private room used for medical treatment.

"When can you do my feet, sir?" asked Joe in a very cultured voice.

I checked my list. "I'm on to the T's now, so I'll be about an hour," I replied. "But, wait a second, what's your name? Are you new?"

"Well, you could say that," he said politely. "I'd be very grateful. . .Wotherspoon's my name - Joseph." He spelled it out in full as I added it to the bottom of the list. "I'll be in the lounge - most grateful, sir," and off he sped, propelling the wheels of the chair for all he was worth down the passage.

When the time came for me to attend to Joe, I walked into the Residents' Lounge to seek him out. It was full.

"Mr Wotherspoon, please," I called out.

Now, either I didn't pay attention to the facial expressions of the residents or they were all jolly good actors. Either way, my request attracted no apparent interest to anyone except Joe, who gave me a cheery, "Coming, sir!"

"If you are new here, sir," I said, "I'll wheel you to the room. It's a trifle complicated."

Joe agreed, once again expressing his gratitude, "You people do a wonderful service."

I was glad that he agreed to remain in the chair for the treatment, as climbing up to the high patients' chair can sometimes be hazardous for handicapped people. As I was washing my hands, Joe said:

"I don't think you'll have much trouble with mine, sir. Really it may not be worthwhile bothering in future. . ."

"Don't worry, Mr Wotherspoon," I assured him, "it's best to have a check. The manager of the home asked me to look at everyone's feet."

"That's just the point," said Joe as I dried my hands, and when I turned round he'd pulled up his trousers, revealing two pink plastic legs! "No, I don't think you'll have any bother with my feet, Mr Vose. . ." His face was like a ripe red pepper and tears of laughter were streaming down his face.

"You can jolly well drive back you old rogue," I told him, as I set off to the lounge to call the remaining patient before tea time.

"They all fall for it," chuckled Joe loudly as he sped down the passage. "Don't let on, sir! I've done it to every

152

chiropodist since I've been here. . .five years. . .but you're the first one to wheel me all the way!"

I was the prize sucker of all and I knew what to expect when I reached the lounge. They just didn't give me a chance to call the final patient's name. The whole place erupted into wild laughter. Joe Wotherspoon had pulled off his favourite jape yet again.

There are, too, those patients who respond to chiropody treatment as if they are theatricals working from a script, their humour is so predictable. I remember Mr and Mrs Smethwick especially well in this sense, and I would make a point of having a little bet with myself that they would trot out the old faithful cracks on every visit. Mrs Smethwick never failed to open with: "I was at back of queue when feet and teeth were given out, Mr Vose. I once asked a doctor if he'd give me something for me feet and he said he wouldn't have 'em as a gift, " and "I'm always tired, me get up and go has got up and went. " I can write it word for word because I heard it so often. But even though she made fun of her own feet, she was always most upset when her husband made disparaging remarks about them - or perhaps she pretended to be upset and this was all part of the act they thought it was their duty to perform in the foot clinic. His prize comment always came when it was his turn to sit in the chair. As his wife was putting her shoes and stockings on he would say, "You'll not see many feet like the wife's, lad. . .I've seen better specimens on a tripe stall. "

Despite my appetite for getting into scrapes, never did I expect to be landed with the age-old predicament of having to escort a drunken man home. Percival Tomkins was a retired waiter and, as far as I was concerned, had the worst feet in Blackborough. He was a most polite and sensitive sort of man and it was not difficult to see how he had reached the heights of his particular calling.

"Please call me Percy, sir, " he had said on the day I met him for the first time, and after the treatment he had presented me with a large Havana cigar - "as a little token of my appreciation, sir. " From his dicky bow down to his highly polished shoes he was the epitome of the head-waiter who had walked the dining-rooms of some of the country's finest hotels. He told me that his arches dropped in the six-star hotel in Bournemouth, and there was a certain pride in his voice as he imparted the knowledge, as if to imply that this was far more acceptable than if they had dropped in a one-star guest house in Redcar or New Brighton.

"The carpets draw your feet, sir, " he would tell me. This remark never fails to bring to mind a cartoon I saw in my student days. A rug was pictured, holding a pencil and a sheet of paper in front of a woman's feet. The caption: 'The Carpet is drawing my feet, doctor'. Probably an inept joke, and what the sufferer actually means by 'drawing' has long been a subject of discussion amongst chiropodists. The popular theory about waiters' feet in particular is that, firstly, they walk on warm, hard kitchen floors as part of their duty. This leads to foot strain and sometimes inflamed conditions aggravated by heat. When they then walk into a carpeted dining-room they are on an un-firm surface, the very opposite to a hard, unyielding tiled floor. A carpet moves when it is stood on; this lack of resistance and stability is not beneficial to feet which are already under stress, and causes strain and muscular fatigue because of the effort which has to be made by the waiter to walk on a moving surface. Hence the balance of the body is affected and there lies the reason for so many splay-footed and hobbling hotel workers, an occupation, in my opinion, second only to the bakery trade in the 'bad feet league'.

Percy had been a martyr to ingrowing toe nails and painful metatarsal corns for many years. He was a nervous patient and certainly didn't enjoy foot treatment, although his relief afterwards was always expressed in the most elegant words of praise. But Percy had a dark secret and, to my cost, I was to find out what it was that very afternoon. Immediately he entered the surgery I knew Percy wasn't the same impeccable Gentleman's gentleman. He had a broad grin on his face and a definite list to starboard. What's more, he smelled of drink. He flopped into the chair and I had to remove his shoes and stockings. Grinning sheepishly, he looked at me with bleary eyes and said in a slurred voice: "I'm sorta. . .sorta. . . sozzled. . Mr. . .sorta Vose. . .Hexcuse. . .oops. . .me. . s. .sir!" But for a change he was as quiet and relaxed as it was possible for a patient to be and just sat back in perfect contentment as I removed the spikes of nail and corns.

After the treatment I made him a cup of coffee and a good swill with water soon had him in a more sober state. He thanked me for the coffee and left, hiccupping ". .oop! . . .do hexcuse Mr. . .oop! Vose. . ." I simply had a good laugh to myself and dismissed the incident as being the result of an unexpected lunch-time drink which had turned into an elbow-lifting session.

Imagining Percy to be sleeping it off at home, I left the

clinic at five o'clock. A familiar figure was weaving in and out of the trees at the far end of the car park - Percy Tomkins the flat-footed, ex-Head Waiter. He was waving his arms at me but when I reached him there was no recognition on his face, just a vacant stare. A whisky bottle protruded from his jacket pocket. My first reaction was to go to the phone box and ring for a taxi but then I realised that I didn't know where Percy lived, and as all the Appointments staff had gone home there was no way of finding out where he lived. I would just have to run him home myself and rely on Percy knowing the way in his present state. Somehow I managed to bundle him into the car and he mumbled something which resembled forty-five Collingford Avenue. Percy's head banged continually on the side window as I drove along, whisky, tobacco and stale beer blending nauseatingly with the petrol fumes that were seeping into the car - I realised this latter was the reason I had got it so cheap. Then, to make matters worse, Percy started to sing at the top of his voice in a crapulent baritone.

"I have heard the Mavis singing her love to the Morn! I have seen a dew drop clinging to a rose just newly-born. . . "

I pulled up outside number forty-five, Collingford Avenue and delighted in the fresh air in my nostrils when the car doors were opened.

"Come on, Mr Tomkins. . .you're home," I said as I helped him from the car and supported him as he weaved his way unsteadily up the drive. The man in the next garden was standing on tip-toes pretending to cut the hedge.

"I have loved her for her beauty but not for love alone!" warbled Percy as he pulled me into a bed of begonias. We reached the front door at last and I rang the bell and almost immediately a voice called out, "Door's open, come in." It was a young, pleasant, female voice. Percy and I negotiated the front door step and then the same voice called out, "Coming, darling. . .you're early, sweetie."

Then a door opened on the landing above and a gorgeous blonde of about twenty-five appeared, clad only in a towel which, even at that distance, didn't prevent me from realising that she was a stunner. Now, when a man is used to looking at geriatric females all day long, a desire to gaze in rapture at this beauty was natural enough. It was like a scene from one of those old Hollywood movies when the desirable young maiden emerges from the river, dripping and nymph-like, awaiting her lover to dry her golden locks. For a beautiful second I was Tarzan and she was my Jane. Then she shattered the illusion by speaking.

"Who the hell are you two? "

"I've brought your father home. . .he's rather. . .well, he's under the weather. . .somewhat. "

"My father! He's been dead ten years. Under the weather, you call it? I call it blind drunk. He's puddled. "

Could she possibly be his wife? "Then he's your husband? " I ventured, hesitantly.

"Is this some sort of joke? " She was glaring at me.

"No, I assure you, " I explained. "He said he lived here. I'm only giving him a lift home. "

"Well, he certainly does not and, what's more, I've never seen him in my life before, " she assured me.

Whilst this exchange was going on, Percy was crawling up the stairs towards her on his hands and knees. He stopped and, looking up at her, said, "My dear young lady, this cheltenham you are addressing is the wery finest chirporist in Blackbugger. . .toe growing in nails or fat feet, madam . . I can weccomend him as a very good chirporist. . ."

"Take this drunk away, do you hear? " screeched the girl before retreating post-haste into the bathroom and locking the door.

On the way back to the car, Percy pulled me all over the garden. By this time the hedge-cutting neighbour's wife had joined her husband and I heard her say, "Fancy, at this time of day, too! "

"I'll join the legion! " bawled out Percy. "That's what I'll do! And in some far distant region where human hearts are fond and true, I will start my life anew! . .Goodbye I go to fight the savage foe. . ."

I couldn't help but marvel at the way he could pronounce his words all right whilst singing, but I have since been told it is common with drunks. "

"For the love of God, Mr Tomkins, straighten up and get in the car! " I hissed in his ear, for we had attracted quite an audience by now. We had reached the passenger door and Percy was actually on the point of getting inside when he suddenly withdrew, pulled out a handkerchief and waved it to all and sundry, singing, "Goodbye. . .Goodbye. . .I wish you all a last goodbye. . .Goodbye. . ." I got into my car, and after a lot of pulling I managed to drag Percy inside from the driver's seat and then reached over to shut his door.

"Now, where do you live? Stop singing and think - please! "

"Live? . . .live. . .number sixty-two. . .no, that's our

156

Bill's. . .number forty. . .oop. . .that's it, number forty."

That was on the other side of the road so I drove for about a hundred yards before pulling up outside the house.

". . .Calderstone Drive, " said Percy when I had switched off the ignition. As my car was one of the early three-wheeler models I had an awful job turning round without a reverse gear but when we had achieved the turn I drove for about a mile in the opposite direction with my passenger crooning softly to himself, "I know I'll be sometimes missed by the girls that I've kissed. ."

Calderstone Drive was a long road but we had only been going for about half a minute when Percy cried: "There you are. . .my house. . . number forty. . . see yonder." His finger was pointing to a signpost, 40 m.p.h. it proclaimed in black paint. I began to think I was lumbered with him for the night. In fact, it was a further half mile up the road before we arrived at number forty-five. A woman's face was staring out of the window and as there was recognition in it, I pulled Percy out and led him up the garden path, confident that this time we were at the right house. A large woman in a black check apron and mob cap opened the door. Her husband was making a great bid to reach her and pulling me all over the path in the process. She was glaring at us in horror.

"Just look what you've done to the lupins! " she said wrathfully.

"I've brought Mr Tomkins home, " I said. I suppose I was stating the obvious, but I had to say something and I didn't know if she was, in fact, his wife. She was.

"Wait till he's sober. . .just wait! And as for you, young man! If you had the job of cleaning him up every time, you wouldn't feed him drink so quick. . .come in, Percival, for God's sake, all the road's watching. You know how they gossip round here. " She eyed me fiercely, "I suppose you think it's funny. " She was just on the point of closing the door on me when Percy spoke up in my defence, at the same time placing his foot in the door to keep it open.

"Chust a minute, Iris. . .chust a minute. . .this chelten-ham is Mr Vose, the chirporist. . .he's the best chirporist in Blackbugger is Mr Vose. . .My fat feet have never been better. ."

"You are a chiropodist? " There was surprise and polite-ness in his wife's question.

"I am, " I answered gladly. "You see, I had to bring him home. He was at the foot clinic. "

"Well! Well! Well! So you are the chiropodist Percival

talks about? " She stared at me almost in wonder. If he'd said I was the Emperor of Mesopotamia she couldn't have been more impressed.

"And a cholly good chirporist! " piped up Percy. "Come in and do the wife's feet. . .she's got fat feet, too, and growing in nail toes. . ."

"Oh, would you, Mr Vose? Do come in, please. "

"Really I don't have time now. . ." I began ". . .you see, I've got to get something for tea. . .before the shops shut and. . ."

"You'll eat with us, " she broke in. "Of course you will. " She was adamant and almost before I knew it I was sitting in an armchair before the fire. Percy fell asleep and Mrs Tomkins and I had tea together, then I treated her feet in front of the fire. Percy woke up just as I was leaving and he was plainly better for having had a sleep. He rubbed his eyes for a few seconds before he recognised me.

"I met Frank Lloyd at lunch time, Iris. . .well, we had a few drinks and. . .well, you know. . ." He looked like a child who had been caught stealing apples from the orchard. His wife beamed at him and there was a giggle in her voice when she answered.

"We know, Mr Vose, don't we? Come home Percy Tomkins, all is forgiven. My, but my feet do feel grand! "

But the golden rule, no matter what form humour may take, is that it is the chiropodist who does the treatments and the patient who does the 'funnies'. I found this out by experience, particularly the time Tom Hancock knocked on the surgery door in his usual impatient manner. He knew that I was treating a patient but would never sit in the waiting room without first letting me know he had arrived. This meant me leaving my patient to open the door because I knew he would keep on knocking otherwise. Tom was the most 'impatient' patient I have ever had, and didn't like to go even a minute over his appointment time. One occasion, on the third rat-a-tat I left my seat and opened the door. Tom's glum, dead-pan face looked me in the eyes.

"I've come for me feet, " he announced dourly.

Three other people were sitting in the general waiting-room at the time so, inspired by the presence of an audience, in a loud voice I replied, "Well, I haven't got them, sir! "

Stony silence greeted my hoped-for howler. Ever since I've left it to the patients and written it all down when they've left.